Open Then The Door

Margaret McConnell

Open Then The Door

FREDERICK MULLER

First published in Great Britain 1967
by Frederick Muller Ltd., Fleet Street, London, E.C.4

PRINTED AND BOUND IN GREAT BRITAIN BY
THE GARDEN CITY PRESS LIMITED
LETCHWORTH, HERTFORDSHIRE

INTRODUCTION

I have often pondered over what it really was that brought about my entry to the convent. Certainly it was not my family, who had thought me too young. It seemed then, and it seems now, that it was something I had decided on many years before. My whole life had centred around a convent since I was very small. The virtues of the life had been held up to me again and again. The Church seemed to regard the religious life as the prime vocation and I had an idea then that marriage was less well regarded by God.

If one thought the religious life was intended by God it was unholy to refuse His calling. There had been no compulsion, no one had ever tried to persuade me to join the order I went to, or any other order for that matter. The advertising was perhaps unintentional. To me nuns had always looked so peaceful and so sure as they went about their work, so convinced that they were right.

Ideals run high when one is young and I was caught up in a fever. To devote one's life to God's work had seemed so easy and all else so useless. I knew very little else, but what I did know seemed so second-rate by comparison with the glorious life I envisaged.

What I expected the inside of the convent to be like I

cannot say. It is impossible to imagine a convent. It is not the building and not the nuns but the strange worldless atmosphere that pervades the place.

If I imagined anything I thought all the nuns would be like those I had known at school. I expected to be accepted in the same way as I had formerly been accepted. I thought I would be able to talk as I had formerly talked. I never thought I would be lonely. When one hasn't been lonely it is impossible to imagine it. The complete separation from my family was not, as I had imagined, a great trial for me. Almost at once I was completely detached as though they had never been.

It was the small things that troubled me from the very beginning. The bareness of the place. The whole convent seemed to be made up of the absence of things I was used to. There were no fires, no flowers, no armchairs, no decorations of any kind. The floors were always without carpets, and the place was continually surrounded by a lack of privacy. One was always on view, there was no relaxing for a moment. A very old nun whom I had known had told me this before I entered, but it was like telling a blind person what they were missing. Until the experience occurs it is impossible to realise it. We can imagine tragedy, it is the trivia which it is impossible to understand, and it was the trivial that made up life in those early years.

My fever of devotion was to suffer many a severe blow, and the reversal of my earlier feelings are understandable to me now, though at the time I was confused. The world was upside down. I had expected to suffer the pangs of martyrdom and all I had to bear was cold water and crowded places. I had expected the peace of angels and found myself turned inside out. Whatever ideals I had were sadly shattered by my own late burst of intellectualism.

Suddenly, and without warning, I started to ask myself the questions that young people in other denominations ask perhaps at an earlier age. I entered the convent with a warm glow and was almost immediately and unaccountably assailed by feelings I did not understand. My feelings were so suddenly changed and I became as cold as the convent itself.

This story is dedicated to all those who are curious about nuns and think of them as beings apart, without thoughts or feelings. It is also respectfully dedicated to the clergy and the superiors of all monasteries and convents in the hope that they will understand that respect for an ideal way of life does not necessarily make the life more bearable to those who leave the world in this period of the twentieth century. Many monastic orders still cling to the antiquated traditions and the old conception of obedience, without thought as to the people who are now coming into the monastic life.

The dual existence of being in and out of the world causes many difficulties which those in authority find hard to understand. Many religious who study in the universities and teach in schools throughout the country are torn between two loyalties.

It is hoped that this story will make the loneliness of some religious people more comprehensible. It is not suggested that all monks and nuns feel the life to be unbearable. This book is simply a plea for a little more understanding, both on the part of the world and those who are in positions of responsibility in the Church.

M. McC.

And, as the Cock crew, those who stood before
The Tavern shouted—"Open then the Door!
You know how little while we have to stay,
And, once departed, may return no more."

OMAR KHAYYÁM

I

I T WAS the beginning of autumn when I came to the convent.

The mustard-tipped trees doffed their leaves and stood like rows of respectful gardeners as the car drove up the path. The cold of the mid-September day bit into me as I moved into the porch of the white building which stood like a plaintive virgin gazing at the green fertile grass. The cumbersome door grunted and unwillingly opened, as though crippled through disuse.

The twelfth day of September was the traditional day of entry to this convent. The hustle of newcomers broke the stillness of the house, and the click-clacking of the sharp heeled shoes re-echoed throughout the convent. Unaccustomed whisperings filled the corners of the monastery, and old nuns beamed at their new insurance, this new security for their old age.

Outside the grey-blue arena of sea frothed backwards and forwards. The gulls knifed the foam and screeched as they swerved to their security of freedom; unhampered they reached the sky, that elusive, untouchable, misplaced blue wall. Inside the convent the grey of the gull was reflected and the austerity conveyed the loneliness of the sea.

On this first day, I had no feelings, but stood watching the fleeting black figures, whose bowed heads and clasped hands seemed to shut me out of their "initiated" world. The clothing ceremony took place almost immediately. The rule expressly forbade the entering of enclosure to any secular except the doctor. The instant change-over from secular to religious reminded me of a conjuror's trick which I had seen many years before, but then it had been a scared rabbit that had been transformed into an enormous stuffed black cat. The coarse black cloth of the dress clung to me, making me doubly conscious of my body in this new world of the spirit. Incredulity and dismay fought with self-conscious embarrassment as I joined the line of novices to receive the kiss of welcome. Standing apart from the others while I waited for the other newcomers to be kissed I marvelled at my feelings. The body-bent rows of nuns did not really alarm me, but rather the sense of incredible aloneness brought about by the disciplined rigidity of the whole gathering. The rows that faced me were made up of women who it seemed to me had become united in a bond of hardship and inflexible and unquestioning obedience to a rule of life. I wondered if this were a surface unity, without emotion or desire for emotion. Feelings had all been pressed down, so I thought, into bottomless depths, and could no longer be imagined, much less experienced.

After the hustle of arrival and a tentative re-orientation to this new life, I, and the other postulants were hurried into the stone church where the community had already gathered for the evening prayers. These prayers which were being droned in the darkness were reminiscent of a Christian prayer wheel. The continual "Pray for us! Pray for us!" rose and fell until it reached a curious rhythm. It was as though each ejaculation pushed the spokes of the wheel

2

a little further, whilst the breathing of the nuns sounded like the last breath of the dying circulating around the chapel until it reached the prayer stall of the "reader", who once more sent out a petition to some saint. Indeed, the final prayer for the departed who had "gone before us" harmonised strangely well with the black carved backs and marbled rosaried hands.

Out of the depths I have cried to Thee, O Lord.
Lord hear my prayer.

As the wailing in the gloom drew to an end a small bell sounded from the back of the blackness. The nuns rose like clustering hens; the clacking of the wooden beads against the carved pews echoed throughout the church whilst they processed down the aisle, the youngest members first.

Once outside the prayer mill I could feel the cold air contrasting pleasantly with the atrophied atmosphere I had just left. Moving in line with the procession I reached the monastic refectory. Here, I knew, was the centre for devotions, penances, spiritual readings, admission and admonition of faults. Devoid of any comfort, the room, with its tables of scrubbed wood, presented a severe picture. The floor was bare expect for the part covering of a frail but highly polished linoleum.

Three tables stood like a balding Trinity, almost totally bare except for the crude white cruets. The nuns were at once separated and united as the Father, Son and Holy Ghost, and like them were as separate in their powers and duties.

The social pattern of monastic life is an enigma in the modern Christian world. The choir nuns who filled one of these bleak boards made up the educated members of the order. The other two tables were filled by novices, like my-

3

self and lay sisters, the two groups sitting at separate tables.

This separating of the working-class sisters from the choir nuns dates back to an earlier century, but the social pattern still remains. To the onlooker it is reminiscent of the second-class citizenship of the Negroes, against whose discrimination the Church has long fought, whilst at the same time almost fanatically clinging to social divisions within her own orders. In this the Church is not cruel but simply blinded by age-old customs.

The rule of these sisters forbade them to rise above their station, yet it was upon these very sisters that the smooth working of the monastery rested. As I looked at them I realised, as I had often done before as a child, that these were the most dedicated and single-minded of all the religious groups. Learning and power were beyond their reach, and work of the most laborious kind their unquestioning lot. Longer working hours, exclusion from the choir nuns' recreation, and different clothes separated them from the major group. A minority of socially lesser origin they had been conditioned for years to accept a humble position, which in any other walk of life would have been seen as degradation and deprivation of privilege. Unable to vote or to carry any influence they had unwittingly perpetrated the master–servant relationship. Heads bent, bodies broken, they had accepted all, demanded nothing, worked until they dropped, and then passed into rest or convenient oblivion.

The lay sisters stood patiently waiting for the intonation of the Grace. Muscular and thickset through years of work they gave the appearance of the Bethlehem ox and ass, devoted and dumb.

"Benedictus, Benidicat . . ." The short grace for the evening meal was soon over and the Martyrology for the on-

4

coming day began to be read. This Martyrology reminded the group of those who had suffered at the hands of the enemy; heroes who had survived the throwing to the lions and died with the name of Christ on their lips.

The burning in fire, the crucifixions with heads down (the last word in ignominy), the beatings, the deprivations of these early martyrs stirred me as I listened through the bustle.

It was during the Martyrology that the initiation began, and I acquired a cup, a spoon, a plate, a knife and fork, the bare necessities which had been placed in a small black box.

So it began—the first silent meal—choking me, killing the purpose of eating. It seemed to me that one of the greatest social acts of man had been degraded to a munching mumble of gums meeting, teeth chewing, a mastication like a slow disease. Bread, butter, eggs—the last main meal before the day ended. The munching and the nerve tearing silence fixed themselves into my mind and made me awkward and aware. The nearby flatulence and stomach rumble became transformed into something grotesque and horrible. The strange signals for the food perplexed me, made me anxious. The closing of the index finger with the thumb, to indicate the need for bread, reminded me of the rabbit-making on the wall when I was a child. Seeing again the shadowed bedroom, the little rabbit opening and closing the recently made mouth, filled me now with an indescribable longing for the past. Bread, I thought, the Staff of Life, the Body of Christ, the Manna of the desert, the food of Angels, and now the answer to a sign. I felt beating in my brain the remembrance from the Book of Kings— "And the Ravens brought him bread and flesh in the morning; and he drank of the brook."

5

It was the belief that the Bread was flesh which had brought me here—that the round white circle was God himself. The fingers went on demanding the basis of the Godhead. The Godhead minus the blessing was being munched in this intolerable silence. It was, I thought, the words that changed the Bread—the Bread that changed the life. Pass the bread, dispel the closed fingers. Pass the ingredients of God and bring back the rabbit. If only I could speak the madness would end; the silence broken the normal would return.

I then turned my attention to the egg. God or the egg? I thought. The brooding hen, like Christ, gathering her chickens under her wing. The eating of the beginning of the hen, the swallowing of Christ in the Bread. All these thoughts coursed through my mind. If only the silence would break, if only Christ would speak to me—if only they could all speak. Dear Christ, if only we would all speak! The rising of the ravens would come soon, the bread, the flesh, the water would be moved away. In the bread and water there was life, in the flesh new hope. New hope of what? I felt that here had begun the death, the death in life. The only living death was being advertised here in this cold room.

A nudge, a swift move of the arm, bringing new signs, new wants. This time the sign was for tea. The cup on the saucer seemed to me like a clown pirouetting on a white balloon. More signs, more demands, more silence, and then the end. Another grace, another thanks for all . . . for what had been given, for what had been taken away.

Another procession, another monumental movement of black bodies. Rows of nuns standing like black railings, self-imprisoned around the white table. As I stood waiting, watching, without sign, I felt too numb to move, to advance

6

or retreat, shocked into the interminable silence that shrouded the place. So, I mused, must have stood medieval man ever mindful of death. So too must he have felt when faced with rows of dead from the plague. There was no life, no hope, all was rigidity, inflexibility, no warmth, no one. Christ, like the will-o'-the-wisp of the old Irish tales, had moved before me, but, as I stretched out my hands He became at once intangible, and to my sight invisible.

"Light of the World enlighten our darkness." Light of lights guide us through this maze. Suddenly, on this first day I began to see the gift of God misunderstood, misinterpreted—life made into a living death.

As I moved out from the refectory to the convent garden I began to realise the implications of my entrance. I was no longer myself, but an unidentifiable Sister Margaret who was now walking in a garden where no man or woman from the world might enter. I was completely cut off, totally alone.

I seemed threatened by a madness as I stood there in the darkness, and I was grateful to it for its cover. I listened to the lost cry of the wheeling gulls and was comforted by them. They seemed so cold and unknown. Cut off from the earth and without companions they glided, these Lethed souls, forgetful of everything. I felt at one with them, and would, if I could, have risen from the garden and floated with them in my billowing black gown into the mystery of the heavens. As I looked up at the blue God-shading wall above me I longed to penetrate it. This wall would never be pierced by cries or tears, but it might be unable to withstand the battering of a small black body as it rose from the ground like a phoenix. If only, I thought, like this bird I had been able to flap my wings and set fire to the body that kept me in life. But even the Arabian bird had been unable to cast off life completely but was forced to start again in the same painful round. The wheel went around and around, there was no escape from the pangs of youth, the pain of old age, the loneliness of death. One was trapped completely—the wheel moved and turned, trundling all living things on the spikes. St. Donatus bearing his lighted wheels must have had more hope. I had no hope, I could not break the wheel; when life was with you it remained; it was impossible to join the gulls and fly off.

Suddenly in a frenzy I prayed. "St. Quintin, pray for me, smash the wheels! Turn off the lights, Donatus! Mother of God protect me! Gate of Heaven give me entrance!"

Half crazed with the impenetrable heavens and the gulls' cries I moved once again into the sombre house. Thrusting down the wildness of the night into the pit of my stomach, I bent my head and clasped my hands in the required manner and joined the small black birds coming home to roost.

At first I did not respond to the "Recreation now, Sister" from the head novice. I found it difficult to associate myself with this namelessness, this black nonentity of sisterhood. The dazed moment passed and I smiled my acquiescence and moved with the other nuns to the common room of the Novitiate. This hour, given by rule for the relaxation of body and mind, was to become for me one of the most difficult hours of the convent life, for it was hedged with rules and regulations. The room itself was one of the most uncomfortable I have ever seen. The high backed chairs, themselves like astringent monks, stood glistening blandly around the table. The austere room was like a barren soul in which nothing could grow or flourish. In one corner of the room stood a statue of the Mater Dolorosa. The mother,

8

weeping at the sight of her battered Son, looked with melancholy at the incoming nuns. I looked at the figure. Poor bastard-born Son of Sin, lying like a marble swan in His mother's arms, even He could not escape from the wheel. It had crushed out His very life's blood. The mother did not cry, she was far past such commonplace.

As I stood there looking at the statue I could hear Peter quite clearly and his words on that last night came back. He had always seemed to me to be obsessed with the pain of life, but now I began to understand him, and I thought briefly about our past friendship.

"It was always the same," he had said. "If they crush you sufficiently you feel nothing in the end. The wheel must get no pleasure in the final round, there is no more suffering, nothing more it can do."

At that moment I wondered if Peter was right. It was hard to visualise him in this room with his kind eyes, and gentle hands and soft voice. Here I was surrounded by the suffering whiteness of the marbled virgin, and even to think of Peter seemed out of place. All the old conversations about the incomprehensibility of pain, and the Eternal Kindness hovered about my mind, but the Gethsemanied hour of recreation had begun. At least the silence was broken, the strictures placed around the conversation did not altogether dissuade the nuns from speaking. The Novice Mistress presided over the group, ready to correct and note faults of speech and gesture.

It was at these recreations that later I was to notice the human element in this regulated life. There was here, as in every other walk of life, the possibility of fatigue, ill temper, misused power, snobbery, favouritism. The Novice Mistress, a disciplined understanding woman of forty, was, for the greater part, above all the human vices, but even

9

she, under the pressure of fatigue, resorted at times to the sharp reproving word.

A maternal figure with tired crinkled eyes and a hint of simple humour she was ideal for the position in which she had reluctantly found herself. She had lived a life of obedience—a life marked by its lack of rationalisation. Of limited intellect and culture she had been able to turn herself into an Ignatian model (for it was upon the rule of this saint that the order was founded). To obey without question was her law, and this was the law she laid down for others. Lacking in personality, it was she who had to lead the conversation on these cold evenings. As to a poor comedian our response was often cold and quiet.

As the room grew warmer and the sewing needles made brisk noises of enjoyment many of the young nuns found themselves betrayed into pitiful and meaningless conversation. The conversation was slow and desultory. The introductions were made again and the cold formal talk began. Sister Bernadette, a tall beautiful nun, spoke to me. "Did you have a good journey?" she asked. "Yes," I replied. There seemed no other answer to the question which asked for nothing but the customary polite reply. I had just completed a journey that meant total separation from my family, my home, and indeed my country. There was much to say, or little, and I chose to say as little as possible.

Suddenly I was learning new names. "This is Sister Ursula," Sister Bernadette said. Sister Ursula turned a round Irish face towards me. "Welcome, Sister," she said, and returned to her sewing. I looked at her stolid country fingers coping with the intricate embroidery, and wondered what she was sewing. "What is it?" I asked. "It's a cotta." She smiled into the white cloth as though she were some

Eastern woman who had been let out briefly into a world that confused her with its turmoil.

I felt as though I were intruding and quickly turned my face to the left where a novice was sitting who looked tensed and strained. She returned my look shyly and told me her name was Sister Angela. She was plaiting a white cord and seemed absorbed in her task. "We are running short of cinctures in the Sacristy." This was her explanation, and for her a tremendous effort at conversation. I became very fond of this girl who was to suffer so much so soon. She had disciplined herself very well they had said, but now I know she had trained herself to become impervious to pain and had retreated to a world that was totally hers except for God.

One novice, with unaccustomed bravery, was reciting an anecdote about a child at recreation. It was an obvious observation which might have been made a thousand times a day by those whose work was with children. Now, however, it seemed to me to be brilliant conversation, the most real life talk I had ever heard. It came as a strange relief in the morgued mumblings that surrounded me. When she had finished the Novice Mistress laughed into the sewing she was holding and suggested that there be a reading from the book. At every recreation when conversation was low they resorted to the book. In time I too became glad there was a book which could cover the hashed conversations and could keep us free from faults.

The story was about a nun who had escaped from Hungary and who had longed to return to her convent. Every so often there was the refrain, "But we were very happy in the convent." The Novice Mistress pointed this out to us often, and in the end I used to await the phrase with my needle poised, and then press the needle into my index finger so no one could see me wincing, and if they did I had at least a rational explanation.

Outside the night darkness hid the convent, the lights of which could be seen from the road and were as torches around a grave. The life within the house seemed as though it were dead or dying, and the lights a trick—a snare of deception.

The hour ended, the tongues like the needles ceased to click when the bell for the great silence was intoned.

The chapel at night was even more cold, more bleak than at the earlier hour. The Examen of conscience was carried out in dim light as though to hide the nuns in their sin from the face of God. Light and dark! I had always imagined the sinful soul dark, and the virtuous soul light, as though God crept into the crevices and lit up the good souls as a reward.

In the weeks which followed I knew God neither came nor went, the soul was neither light nor dark, the reality of nothingness was borne in on me.

God was boxed up in the altar like some chained animal, and He gave no comfort, no sign of existence. There was no movement, just a squared vision of eternity behind a gold curtain. It had been wanton of God to shut Himself up, to have made Himself so round and small, melting at the salivating touch of his servants.

Why standest Thou afar off O Lord? Why hidest Thou in times of trouble . . . ?
I cry unto the Lord but He does not hear me.

To what had Christianity reduced the Godhead? Why had it trapped Him like a rabbit in a snare? The old magicians had transformed the majesty of God. At a word they had robbed Him of all dignity and placed Him in the box, but now it seemed they could not remember the magic formula; those who had so cleverly placed Him there could not retrieve Him. The trick had overcome the conjuror and Christ was out of my touch, out of my sight, and I was left in the small brown pew mumbling prayers, words of expectation and hope, like a child at Christmas.

The bulwark of Christianity had disappeared behind the curtain like a reluctant actor fearful of recall. It seemed to me then that the Bread was crumbling, and dropping, crumb by crumb, to the ground.

Another bell sounded in the darkness. Already I was beginning to feel allied to this sound, even if it did only end one sensation to start another. The bell ended everything, though it was possible to imagine it began everything. They rang the bell even when one died; then it was difficult to distinguish, I thought, whether it was for the end of life or the beginning of another.

The chapel left, the hour of the Great Silence was begun. Only the scuttle of shoes and the tinkling of water jugs broke the stillness. The darkness of the late day had now given place to the black of the night. I stood in the cubicled match-box room listening to the sounds. The movement of the feet; the sound of the water washing the many bodies seemed like a terrible baptism. Another future focused day was ending. The days here would be like foetus in the womb, feeding and existing in anticipation only of the life to come. When would it begin, this life in the presence of the God released at last from His wooden box?

> *When will the night be gone that comes*
> *With the fading light? When will the dawn arise*
> *That brings new hope?*

I was comforted by the perplexity of the psalmist and fell into a lonely sleep.

2

EACH MORNING the bell ringing in the darkness awoke the convent. Sometimes it was as though the night had been too tired to change into the day, and wearily had retained the status quo. As I arose from kissing the ground according to the monastic custom I felt the small dusty fluff on my mouth. As a child I would have thought this would have broken the communicant's fast, but now it simply filled me with nausea. At five o'clock we kissed the ground, all of us in the dormitory, and the prayer of we twenty went up to the heavens, and the warning of the imminence of death was noted.

> *Remember man thou art but dust and into dust*
> *Thou shalt return.*

The general morning prayers were followed by the dressing. The cincture, the symbol of purity that coiled around the body like a prison cord; the cape, denying the truth of womanhood, and the veil which hid the hair of all the nuns and distorted the feminine features.

Every morning when I entered the chapel I found it full of black bodies, as though they had never moved from there. In the midst of all this the sanctuary light gleamed.

The shone brass gave the appearance of gold, and the red glow the appearance of warmth, but there was no gold and no warmth. The lamp was a focal point, a reminder that He was still boxed above the altar. In this greyness of the early mornings I began to feel my faith flickering like the light in the brass. The futility and coldness of it all forced me to kneel in dumb amazement. This timetabled existence began gradually to weary me. The drowsy hour of the early morning would later give place to the distracted hour of midday, and later the night vigil of weary waiting for release.

After every meditation the Mass began with its joyful psalm.

Introibo ad altare dei
Ad deum qui laetificat
Iuventutum meum.

"To God who gives joy to my youth." One morning the meaning of these words struck me forcibly. "To my youth, to my youth"—the lines moved before my eyes, an ironic drinking song. I needed only the goblet to drink to its passing.

The priest was taking up the cup and saying, "Accept O Eternal Father Almighty . . ." The priest, with blue white hands, seemed like an old wizard performing an ancient rite.

Up above his head he was holding the host like a trophy, man victorious over God, and holding Him above the crowd well caught between arthritic fingers. Rounded into a circular existence God was upstanding for inspection, looking down at the genuflected knee and bowed head.

The wine too was quickly transformed, as though inviting Christ on the Cross to drink His own blood. Bend-

15

ing down from the Cross He ignored it, gazing with wooden stare at the faces before Him. Here He saw His wheat rising from the ground, rows of black bread spread before Him.

Now I myself was joining the long line of those who were to take part in the cannibalistic Feast, and I joined the queue so that I might swallow in one mouthful the wafered God.

Dislodging the melting Host from my teeth I felt a compassion for the Jews who had not been able to comprehend this little God. Why had He chosen this outrageous way? Why had He found it necessary to make a new myth? Fable or myth, truth or tale, it was on this I had based my life, this was the reason for my early vigil, for the pains of the hard kneeling board which supported me, for the whole damnable trial that was before me.

The morning meals, like the evening meals, were a collection of signs and silence. Cold porridge, like the belly of a frolicsome fish, slithered around my saucer. Bread and more bread—I was completely surrounded and possessed by the bread.

On this particular day, lifting my eyes I stared at the table-turned faces. Turned down; always the faces were turned down, as though they could not reach the ground soon enough. The awful silent chewing passed from mouth to mouth. It was the silence that was so overpowering. The owlish black bodies bent over the food were tearing at the centre of my nerves. I felt I could bear it no longer. I took their wretched bread, which was curling up on the plate with a look of disdain, and threw it on to the table. It was like hurling God Himself into their midst. It was as though I had crumbled their life's mainstay in the throw. As I saw the bread move from my hands I thought at least that the

16

cage of oppressive silence would splinter in their eyes and crash to the ground. But the eyes and the faces did not change, the monastic framework was untouched by my hysterical outburst. The crying, the rebellious, those maimed with total despair were not heeded. All remained silent, sorrowful perhaps at the outrage, but silent.

I raced from the room and escaped on to the steps of the building. Standing on the steps I looked down on to the garden which so often before had been my sanctuary. To-day even the garden looked unfriendly. The air was cold. The leaves which had fallen did not want me—a traitor. I felt like Judas escaping from the Room, with the Bread ruined and broken up before the eyes of His followers. I could feel the water in my eyes, and the sweat trembling on my body, and yet I could not go back. I hated them all, I could not achieve what they asked, I had never known that this was what it was like. Noiselessly, hating and wondering, I stood empty and lonely, like a mother after birth, empty, pathetic.

"Sister. Come here!" The Novice Mistress, brimful of a faded understanding, awaited my approach. Then we walked, like the East and West, divided worlds that could not touch, until we reached the Novitiate.

When we entered the room she made a movement with her hands as though she were about to pat some little animal that had strayed in for comfort.

"Kneel down, child," she said, and settled herself comfortably into the great chair which boomed out its superiority as she touched the springs.

I knelt down in the customary position like a dog expecting its bone. I waited for the word of dismissal, but it did not come. From my position of disadvantage I saw a mass of black covered knee on which were clasped hands that looked like embracing peaches. I think it was the attempt at understanding that was the most difficult thing to bear.

"Come now, child, what is it all about? What is the matter? Can you not settle?"

There seemed to me to be so little I could say in defence, there was no excuse for what I had done. To try to explain would have made the whole thing even more incomprehensible. She was used to everything following a well-ordered pattern. She had been conditioned to a way of life that had little room for the extravagance of hysteria.

At this moment the last thing I wanted to do was to enter into a discussion with her. All I wanted was to be free of her, of the indefinable them whom I considered to be responsible for my being there at all.

I said nothing in reply, I could think of nothing to say, and her voice droned on. She was repeating to me what she had said to many others before. It was like a sermon she had learnt by heart.

"Control, control, child, is what you must strive for." I looked at her hand waving like a magic wand over a naughty elf.

My eyes had all this time been cast down to the floor, and I could feel the hate surging into them as her age old formula was thrust down my throat. I wondered, for the first time, what control really was. It served as a blanket to feeling. It covered one's nakedness on the outside, but the painful rawness of the inside was not really protected by it.

"All this control," I said, "it is deception, it's a lie. One is living a lie if one behaves all the time contrary to one's feelings."

"One is living like an animal when one acts as one feels,"

18

she replied. "Life would be impossible in a community if everyone behaved as they felt. Control your moods and all will be well." She turned away from me then as though the interview were over.

I felt foolish and embarrassed on my knees without one word I could utter in self defence. I felt even worse as I began to realise that what she had said was true. Life in a community of women would be unbearable if everyone was to act as the mood took them. I began to think of why I had come. In the past when I had thought of the convent life I had not really thought of the people at all, but had been urged on by some feeling of dedication to God. God had been the only thought in my mind, and I tried at this moment to recapture those early feelings, but in the grim reality of the pious life I felt defeated. Yet, I thought, God must require this. I rose to go, but struggled awkwardly to my feet in the cumbersome clothes, like some kind of fumbling circus bear. God it seemed had pushed me into the arena and could keep me there by tempting me with infrequent drops of honey. The mainspring of this new life, was it the honey of the gods, or was it the drug of betrayal? There was no answer to the question.

When I reached the door the Novice Mistress called me back and held out a letter to me. The first letter in many weeks, and I rushed forward to take it. As soon as I held it I noticed that it had been opened. I gasped involuntarily, all the new found control deserting me. "Why, it's open," I said.

"Oh, yes, Sister, all the letters are opened here. It's the rule. The same for everyone you know." She smiled her dismissal, and I turned to go. This invasion of privacy was past anything I had ever thought or imagined. Such a censorship was impossible to understand or forgive.

3

THE ROUTINE labour of the day was beginning when I joined the lines of silent women. They were all industriously employed as though the cleaning gave them an outlet for their feelings. This was the kind of work at which I had always showed a special incompetence, and there was nothing now to make me feel that there was likely to be any change, or that I was ever likely to excel. I tried in the early days of my training to try and get through the whole laborious business as quickly as possible. I soon learnt that this was of no use as one had simply to wait at the task until the appointed hour was up. I felt at times like another Christ nailed at the task until the hour when it all was consummated and I could be free of it all.

I mentioned one day to Sister Bernadette that the whole rigidity of the timetable was artificial.

"We keep at the work," I had said, "as though it's the keeping to the timetable that makes the work meritorious and not the love of God that lies behind it."

She looked at me, her brown eyes filling with hurt astonishment and said, "It's the discipline that's important, Sister. You must learn the value of this denial of urges."

"But can't you imagine," I said, "some outraged Jew

propping Christ up with the nefarious concoctions that they used to keep prisoners alive? They had to make Him keep to the timetable. Was it the love of us or the keeping to the timetable that was important?"

"He fulfilled the Will of God. That is all of any importance in this life."

Sister Bernadette was one of the most perfect people I have ever met, and I learnt not to express my liberal views in front of her.

She did the most delicate embroidery and played the organ like an angel, and denied every humane thought that came into her head. She lived by the rule book and the bell and considered all distractions outside of these as useless. Yet there is no doubt that she was the most beautiful woman I have ever seen. She had a long willowy body and slender tapering fingers, and a face with the beauty that only a nun can have.

She must have known she was beautiful and yet one could never tell. I never really liked her, for it was like living with the Archangel Gabriel. I felt so imperfect all the time. I wondered, at first, if there were anyone else with such imperfections and such wild, liberal ideas as myself.

I could think clearly some days and feel sure it was not Sister Bernadette's fault, she was simply the product of a way of life. A sort of public school image, where Christ was the Dean and the Novice Mistress the headmistress. They moulded her, and indeed all of us, but with me there was little success. I was a natural failure from the start.

We followed a routined way of life based on the rule of St. Ignatius. "A wonderful scholar, saint and soldier," the Novice Mistress had told me. "Be disciplined like him and you won't go far wrong."

"I could never be disciplined like him," I had said to her.

"Make it your aim, child. Strive for what you know to be valuable and be sure you arrive at your goal. God will help you."

I began to feel like some polio victim on a forty-mile march. How could God help me to be what I despised?— an automaton, a runner after the rule, a little black golliwog on a string that could be pulled here and there at the slightest tinkle of the bell.

Every hour had its own brand of spirit breaking. No one was allowed to indulge in any occupation for more than an hour. There was one thing allowed to us, the garden walk, and I learnt to dread it in the winter.

I first learnt about this routine from Sister Anthony who had seen me reading my book *The Practice of Christian and Religious Perfection* in the warm room near the cloakroom.

"We must go to the garden for the reading, Sister," she said. Her voice was very gentle as though she hated to inflict pain on anyone, and as though she had a special insight into what one would feel before they had even been aware of the feeling.

"We walk up and down and do our reading there. It's good exercise and one soon becomes used to it."

"I object to this pantomime performance," I replied.

"You must try to get used to it because they will be there nearly always when you are in the garden. If you choose your own particular path and walk up and down it each day it soon becomes like home and you will quite enjoy it."

She gave me a tentative smile as she moved away as though to have given an assured one would have been irreverent.

I had chosen my own small path and wandered up and

22

down it at the appropriate hours like a sturdy policeman or a happy prostitute. I never dared mention this last thought to anyone, but I thought often of the prostitutes who stayed in the main square at home. I had once taken up a beat by mistake outside a huge store whilst waiting for my mother. An elderly and much painted prostitute had come up to me and told me to clear off in terms that had never been uttered in this sacrosanct ground. I did think of that woman sometimes as though both of us had some kind of common tie. I could never be sure whether it was the prints on the small beat or my awareness of our lonely lives. Whatever it was, I prayed for her and felt virtuous on my path.

We read the lives of the heroic early fathers who had gone before us in the desert. These were lives of perfection, these were the lives we were to emulate. I talked one night to Sister Anthony about the hermits and we became closer friends after that. She didn't say much but she listened as though she really wanted to hear what one had to say. I noticed this because I have often thought that when most people listen it's like a play. They wait for you to finish your lines and then jump in as though they were fearful the prompter will get in before them.

"They threw back the life God gave them in His face," I said.

"How do you mean?"

"They let themselves die slowly and gloomily in the desert when they should have lived out the life He gave them in happiness and fruitfulness."

"I understand St. Jerome," she said. "I've been reading his life lately."

"That cave man. That masochistic stone breaker!" I exclaimed.

"Don't say that, Sister," she gently remonstrated.

"But you must admit it, Sister, that useless withdrawal, what good did it do to God?"

"There is no good we can do to God. He is all Good and does not need actions but intentions. He wants us to do for Him what we feel is right for us. Look at Stylites and the wonderful life he led."

"That unhygienic trapeze artist. His virtue was so perilous he had to rest it on a pole."

I was shocked at my own vehemence, and so was Sister Anthony. I thought then that I had lost a good friend, but she simply remarked, "You must be careful of what you say, Sister. Everyone will not understand that you mean no harm, no irreverence."

I had not meant to offend her and tried to change the conversation to more general lines.

Later that night I went into the garden and thought about the hermitic souls who had passed a life of lonely desolation. I felt guilty that I had spoken so irreverently about lives which were so obviously heroic and worthy of imitation.

They had suffered the loneliness, these mistaken souls. There was, I thought, no need of desert, one dwindled to a nonentity soon enough, clutching the loneliness which began in the bowels of one's being and then submerged, finally and completely, the last dregs of personality, of God-given joy in life. They piled up temptation, sadistically and systematically, these men of God, and then devoted themselves to the conquest of the sin which tormented them. Looking up at the sky I imagined the pole rising to God, the seagulls circling the drained saint on his pylon a monstrosity in the heavens; a monstrosity to all but God —who loved His bait blowing on a rod in the wind.

24

Did Stylites think to tempt God? Did he think to tempt Him to fish below? This saint, this neurotic mistakenly diagnosed by the church. He who joined the heavens in life, and looked from his heavenly eyrie on the misshapen brethren below.

Suddenly I felt a surge of empathy with this perched animal of abnegation as he twisted in vision before my eyes. His particular madness had sent him scaling up the line in an attempt to see his God. "Lonely little neurotic, pray for me!" I exclaimed. "St. Stylites, lift me with you to the clouds!" My sympathy for him began to grow in these lonely hours in the garden. His isolation touched me and began the beginning of my insightful life.

I began to see myself in relation to the world, no less strange to mine than Stylites to his. I had become an outsider, a refugee, an escapist. Could I, I wondered, join the bands of the desert? These old men with stones and fasts and furies at their heads became an increasing reality for me. I began to understand this world of swimming temptation. I saw them, like myself, casting out each devil as it assailed them. Lifted suddenly for a moment into this glorious gathering, all was forgotten, warmth filled me, my steps quickened, and the numbed hands holding the book in the icy garden were the beginning of my desert.

Mortify the body so that the soul might live; Plotinus had thought this long before these men of iron. This remedy of the saints and philosophers would serve me too. From this glorious hour, this Pauline moment of conversion, I was sure that I would never turn back. Eagerly I turned myself to the mortification of the body which would bring death to the flesh and life to the spirit. The real life, the life of the soul.

Truly I thought with the psalmist:

25

My feet were almost moved: my steps had well nigh
slipped ... but Thou hast held me by my right hand.
And by Thy will hast Thou conducted me,
With Thy glory Thou hast received me.

Now, at last, I could open my arms to every pain and
deprivation. These lean hours, these months of endurance
would bring me the control I needed. Then, at last, they
could read my letters and munch their bread, but I would
not give in.

St. Simon, patron of the desolate, pray for me!

My desert, my withdrawal, my hermitic era had begun.

4

IT WAS in such a way that my war on the body began. The "discipline", the traditional thrashing cord of the monastery, became my closest friend. This small white whip of flagellation became the symbol of my conversion. This whip would beat the caged monster within me; we would win, the little white whip and I.

This then was my drug, my morphine against the old feelings. In the little square boxed room the cord bit into my bare shoulders. The pain moved slowly at first, and then hotly through the unaccustomed bared body. If in its falling the cord lost some of its strength this was natural. The time would come when the fall of the cord would be as swift and savage as the rise, and this yellow cowardice would finally vanish. At last, for the first time since my coming, I was happy, deliriously so. I was lifted, elevated from the shallow emptiness of the world, I had joined a group, a legion of souls who had thrown off the restrictions and were racing up the ladder of Jacob to the Almighty, Everlasting, Ever Watchful God.

As the weeks passed the pain of the "discipline" was increased, the number of strokes rose with painful accuracy. The anticipation was the worst. I could feel the pain when

I rose on the Saturday morning. This was the day, the day I dreaded and longed for at one and the same time. I thought long about the scourging of Christ. As I did the morning duties I spoke with Him. Remembering His painful scourging I took courage—what little it was I offered Him in compensation.

I had often wondered about the doctrine that the Church taught us concerning suffering.

I spoke to the Novice Mistress one day during the afternoon advice period in order to try to convince myself of the benefit of this to God. I was beginning to understand the benefit to myself. I was learning the importance of discipline as a virtue in itself, but I wanted to feel that it was giving pleasure to God.

She repeated the age-old doctrine I had learnt as a small child.

"There is no time with God. We make up to Him now for the Agony He suffered in His life. In the Timelessness of Eternity our present and past acts are there in God's sight. When He was in agony in the garden He saw you and was glad you thought of Him, it made up to Him for the thoughtlessness of the world."

I wondered what she really thought, or indeed if she had ever thought of anything. She was like a vending machine, always pushing out little drawerfuls of the expected, and I wondered if she had any idea of what Christ was like. Had she ever visualised that bedraggled vagrant as He hung on the pillar? I tried to draw the picture for her, but she seemed to be so confined, so unable to understand.

"He was a battered little man holding on to the pillar like some drunken beggar. Why was it necessary for Him to suffer like that? What was wrong with God that He had so to make Christ suffer? Was God a sadist that He had to have His pound of pleasure from even His very Son?"

There followed on this a very tortuous argument dealing with the Divinity of Christ, the Godhead of the Christ was placed forward with every detail. For me it made little difference to the situation. If God had done this to Himself to satisfy Himself He was a masochist, and not merely a sadist. His sadism came when He demanded continually from us what had given Him pleasure, but what was to us merely pain. Insight into the question seemed to diminish after this doctrinal conversation. But I wondered about the man Christ as He swayed by the stone pillar clutching His small garment of modesty. None of the platitudes would ever explain away the question of the lonely Christ.

What worried me most of all was that my control decreased. The anticipation of the "discipline" had caused me to twitch and become more wretchedly sensitive and nervous; my feelings were raw, more painful than the aching shoulders.

I wondered too about the other novices, and became gradually aware that there were many more people for consideration than the few novices I had come to know at first. I began to be able to distinguish their faces and their walks, but there wasn't very much opportunity to talk with them. The recreation hours were brief and supervised, and as a general rule there was little speaking outside of the appointed time. Even so, I gradually felt I knew them well.

Sister Catherine, a morose woman with a sallow complexion and dark eyebrows which were always crinkled into a worried expression, seemed to me an unlikely candidate for survival. She was, in the first place, older and more cultured than the rest of us, and must have found our conversation infantile. She had taken her degrees at the university before her entry and was, therefore, a person of what we considered to be immense worldly experience. She was, in fact, what I have since learnt is the world's general opinion of nuns, a frustrated spinster who had left her home after a broken engagement and had tried her luck in the field where love was reputed never to change. The Eternal and Ever steadfast love of God was her last hope, and she was failed in the end even by Him. Before the fatal day however she was a good friend of mine. She had a dry sense of humour which she decorated with a permanent sniff, which I first thought was an expression of disdain. But I learnt later that it was the result of nothing more sinful than a default of the nasal channels. She was lonely the day she came, and went away with the tremendous sense of failure which she carried as an added burden for many years.

She was one of the few people with whom I could discuss the unnatural feeling I sometimes felt about the penances and mortification. I only realised her disgust when quite by chance we sat together at recreation at the end of the table. The opening of the conversation was difficult. She was sewing a small piece of black cloth, and this caught my attention.

"What is it you're making?"

"You know quite well what it is."

I looked again and realised that I knew only too well what it was, and felt foolish for asking. She noticed my confusion, and after exploiting the difficulty of the nasal channels gave me a smile. She had beautiful teeth.

"I don't know why you make such a depressing thing at recreation. There are surely more cheerful jobs you could find?"

"If I don't there are more depressing times when I would

have to make it. I am making them for everyone and hate to do it during the silent sewing period."

I noticed her hands were shaking and felt sorry for her. She was making the cover for the discipline rod, and knew that when she had completed her task every young woman in that room would have the rod covered by the black cloth.

"Do you use it?" she asked.

"Of course I do, doesn't everyone?"

"Not always. Not if you have the dispensation."

"How do you get it?"

"The Mistress will give it to you if you need it."

"Why should you need it?"

"Because there are days when it will pierce you so hard that you can never lift it again. There will be days when the thought of it will make you shiver as soon as you wake. You will find your hands shaking and your body cringing, and then you learn not to despise the dispensation."

"I don't despise those who have the dispensation, I just wondered why."

"Those who give up the discipline try to take on something else instead."

"But why must they do something else? If they are too ill to continue they should stop."

A gigantic sniff came as a reply to this remark, and the needle sewing the cover stopped.

"You will learn that the rule in every monastery is to go forward and any backsliding is forbidden. We are committed to a life of perfection."

I felt cold as she said this. She obviously did not believe one word she was saying. She was forcing herself to accept the rule the Novice Mistress had laid down as the goal of the perfect religious. I wanted her to enumerate the alternatives to the discipline because I knew that if there was an alternative I might accept it for a time.

"There are always the nettles, and the fasting, and the Confessor will give you suggestions if you want them."

She went on sewing, and the sniff came and went absent-mindedly. She was a gentle cultured woman being forced into the mould. She was almost too old; the moulding must come in youth or the pain is nearly always too great. This was something I did not know then, but I knew her difficulties were much greater than mine, and I had a warm feeling for her. In the end the sniff seemed to take on a personality, and at times I thought we three made a happy group. She looked for me often at the recreation but we could never choose to sit next to one another, this was forbidden, so I did not always talk to her, but we often had a glance that made me feel less alone.

In the early morning I broke the ice in the washing water and let the cold drops trickle down my wounded shoulders. I hated the morning; sitting on the little bed I longed for rest, for sleep, but the bell always woke me. They had said that if one genuinely overslept it did not matter; but I always awoke. There was no morning I could remember of these Novitiate days which did not start with the aching tiredness that soon became as much a ritual of rising as washing and dressing. I longed for sleep, and would have given all I possessed for one long rest. But I could not give in.

For a long time it was the silence that was the most onerous. It strained me in a way that no other restriction of the life did. The pains of tension spread from my head to my breast and then to my stomach, but there was no going back; I had chosen my road and would walk along it until I collapsed.

With the pains there came, too, an increased awareness of people and things. I waited in agony for the "chapel sniffer", in the dormitory for the "shuffler", and in the refectory for the "burper". They all set themselves up as my executioners, but I would not give in. These virtuous, pulsating torturers would not break down my desert of improvement. I was safe in the desert; the Sun might at some time burn me with His heat, but I could bear the ensuing thirst for Him who had so thirsted for me.

When the silent meals became less of an agony, and the unnatural gathering together became more commonplace, another form of penance presented itself. This was the "scrap plate". Now it was not the silence that troubled me, but the wasted food gathered together on the plate. It passed each member at the table like a miscellaneous collection of sins, and it revolted me; it lessened my appetite as well as aesthetically distressing me. When finally I had conquered this I felt there was no victory I could not obtain. In the early days of the Novitiate the kissing of the feet of the gathered community had, in turn, sickened, frightened and disgusted me. Now the crouched procession no longer disturbed me so wretchedly. The procession, which had symbolic merit, and was a long standing tradition, was carried out each week. As I stood there it seemed to me that centuries of huddled nuns moved past me, whilst others proffered the well-shod black feet.

At these times I became an observer again, unwillingly, almost unwittingly, setting myself apart. I was like a frigid woman, carrying out the form of the act without joy or sorrow or hate. I hated these outward signs, these Judaic remains in the new religion of the new law. Standing there as they moved past me, each one comprehending the shell-like ceremony in her own way, I wondered at their thoughts, and wished I could find courage to discuss it with some of the other novices.

The opportunity came one day when there was a centenary celebration. We were all sent to the kitchens to prepare the grapefruit for the celebration meal which would be attended by the hierarchy and all the priests of the surrounding parishes. There were guests from many parts and the grapefruit preparation was a long job. We were given permission to talk as we worked and as the Novice Mistress was required for the "parlour" where many of the guests had already arrived the conversation was freer than would normally have been the case. My group consisted of Sister Anthony and Sisters Ursula and Catherine, and another novice with whom I had little conversation. Her religious name was Imelda and she was an alert, unusual girl.

The difficulty with conversation in the convent was that one became so used to the continual silence it was difficult at first to begin talking, and when the conversations really began there was the difficulty of waiting whilst everyone had a chance to speak. The etiquette of the convent was very strict on this point, and one had to wait with perfect patience until whoever was speaking had finished.

Sister Catherine was wrenching the grapefruit apart with a curiously blunt knife. She sniffed at the removal of each seed and looked disconcerted when the fruit splashed on to her fingers.

"These miserable seeds look like the shoe-hiders." Sister Imelda mumbled something about the grapefruit having the same acidity as that select group.

I took my opportunity; it might never have come again, and I was delighted I was with this group.

"It's just a hypocritical routine," I said.

"A psychological circus you mean." Catherine, as I later

called her, had lost her sallow look and was glowering at the seedless grapefruit.

"They stand there like reluctant Cinderellas whilst we grovel around. What kind of humility is that for heaven's sake?"

"Maybe they think they can convince us they feel too humble to have us kiss their feet." I said.

"They know we have to." Sister Imelda had stopped looking mild and was squirting fruit juice ferociously into a bowl.

"Anyone would think they had never been novices the way they make things so difficult for us." The usual sniff followed this pontifical assertion and we were all very quiet for a little time. We had not spoken so freely since our arrival and felt guilty.

I saw again the pinched virgin faces of the "shoe-hiders" as they withdrew their feet as the novices approached and then forced them to follow the feet that were disappearing covered by the rags of abstracted lowliness. One could easily tell those who would take part in the charade, and had it not been for the blood-shattered feet of Christ, neither I nor the other novices would have been able to endure the impossible, grotesque exhibition of humility. I allowed myself for a time to drift off into a kind of biblical dream.

Let them walk on me and press me into my desert, they could not touch me now. The sand dunes and the blistering sun would protect me, they would not follow me into this land. Neither goat nor sheep, nor the donkey of Christ would have the foolishness to carry them there. With the Sun I was safe. In the waters of a new Babylon I had swum, and there was no crossing, no stick or rod could break down these waters that flowed from a spring of truth.

35

The life I led then was one of solitude and it was a comfort when the groups oppressed me, and a wasteland when the old world sent in the song of past time—the abode of the wilderness, where the animal was tamed and broken; where the spirit drank of the river and asked no more. I did not want to see the river of blood He had sent throughout the land; the Sun would dry it as the season of penance passed. The enemy that had trodden on me in the day had passed, leaving His blood swilling in the mire, but I had washed in the blood, and the covering of my body was the blood that ran because of the slaughter by the enemy who had kicked Him with these feet, and then pierced The Feet like crossed hands on the cross.

I thought suddenly about the meal-begging, an old monastic penance dating back so far I could not recall a time when it had not been in history. They went, these well-fed, well-shod nuns from table to table, like itinerant friars of old, begging for "God and Our Lady's sake" to be given something to eat.

Squatting on the floor these images and likenesses of God changed mysteriously into little huddled Buddhas, and ate the meal in this uncomfortable posture.

Here the brides of Christ ate of His table in the wilderness. Their beauty was not seen, and Christ Himself had been cast from the banquet. Dressed in Truth His clothes were not fitted for the revelry. Wherefore hast Thou gone O Christ? Why have the enemy taken over? Why do they seek to hide You behind a covering of virtue that has lost its truth, O bringer of Truth?

We had almost finished the grapefruits when I realised I had really missed my opportunity to discuss one of the aspects of the life that troubled me most. Sister Catherine was drying her fingers on a cloth, and scowling, whilst Sister

Imelda was busily resuming her look of mildness and other worldliness as I came quietly out of my trance. We had finished earlier than we had anticipated, and I went to the garden outside the kitchen.

Small poverty-hushed groups, adrift between two worlds, waited outside at the wall for the remains. A lay sister came out with bread and cheese wrapped in the huge apron as though she were sprinkling crumbs for the birds. This I thought was no longer a mime, this was the reality. I saw poverty as a whining acquiescence of transparent gratitude, and I felt for them. The merchants of paucity bartered at the door. Accustomed to their chatter the lay sister took little notice of their "A mass for yer, Sister". "God bless ye, Sister." The phrases dropped like coins in a slot and the machine pushed out the ration.

They huddled together. One man in particular I remember. He had his bowl held close to him with one hand, and the other sleeve of his jacket flapped with hungry anticipation. He was a war victim. The vacant sleeve was his mark of glory, his honourable claim to everything that life could give him free. The others in the group were just dishevelled, disordered life refuse. They had no claims on the nuns, and for this reason they effaced themselves in the greyness of the protecting wall.

The strong Irish lay sister was used to them and treated them all alike. Dunkirk victims and idle tramps were dealt with briskly and hurriedly so that she could get back to her work. Sometimes she called in one or other of the men to help her carry the waste food to the bins. On these occasions the lucky few ate their meal in the dignity of the sparkling clean kitchen. Unless they were helping in this way they were treated in the manner of starving fowl that had clucked or cackled out their need at the back of the house.

These were the images and the likeness of God to whom we threw out bread with majestic gestures, as though we were God sending down the manna. What was it Christ had said? "They were always with us."

Was it God's inversion or ours? Had He thought to fill the rich with poverty in spirit and the poor with desire? What, anyway, was desire? I had always wondered about real desire. I had never really desired anything until now. There had been no strength in my wishes before. Previously I had been, and that had been sufficient for me, but now I wanted freedom, a life unhampered by pride or feeling, a desert life where one was neither rich nor poor, where there existed no one but God. I wanted an existence where there was not only no poverty but where the magician, the keeper of the box, caused all these material things to vanish in the air, the trick of tricks, leaving a scene of solitude and freedom, Life existing with mortality, a living death existing with Life. It was for this I had striven since my coming and they had not really understood. Their emphasis was on rule, on the observance, everything was in sight. The hidden was kept secret, and they were forced to keep the outward show. This was difficult for me. The part in the circus did not suit me, the part of a clown was difficult.

"It is the clown who is always the most tragic figure," my father had once told me. I remembered too a story of a clown who had juggled before a statue of the Virgin in order to please her. How lonely he must have been, since she was the only one who had understood his little magic in a world based on the skill of the magician. The magician had to be approved, ordained according to the book. They took no notice of you when you were not regulated. "Poor unregulated juggler, perform for me! Matriarch of clowns, accept my performance!"

The meaning of the life I had undertaken began gradually to become comprehensible to me. The suffering of the body, the total capitulation of rights, the absence of privacy, and the pain of the overbearing power of others began finally to cause me to make a complete surrender, not of the body only, but of the mind also. As I felt the ability to obey commands and stem feeling increasing so also I felt the life and warmth inside me grow less.

The body had ceased to trouble me, but the mind had, in its perversity, set up a masquerade which taunted me. I was beginning to relish pain; my righteousness and virtue cavorted before my eyes like little devils at a dance. Naked they waltzed before me. I could feel the very basis of my life being threatened. My heroic penances moved like freshly painted tarts to taunt me. My mortification had become a luxury I shouldn't have enjoyed. Forced to seek advice from the Novice Mistress, I found they expected me to cut out the drug. They wanted the roots of my existence out, they wanted the tree cut down; they could not wait to prune, the wood must go completely.

The Novice Mistress accused me of pride which she saw as the worst sin. It was impossible for me to explain that leading such a life this was something which was almost inescapable. She saw sin as a disease for which there was only a very painful cure—like a cancer it must be cut out at the very roots.

The cure was perilous and a convalescence would bring me out of the desert to their world of rule, to their ideal. But the sore grew, and I knew I would have to leave my haven and walk again in their land on the neatly cut flag-stones of their ruled life.

Later, when I had left the desert, there was nothing on which I could rest or fall back. I was alone again with their rule and their aspirations which did not satisfy me. I began to feel the new madness encompassing me.

The devil on the discipline-bag jumped like a pet parrot on to my shoulders, and then I knew the painful beatings could be no more. Where could I go? What could I do? He had deserted me and left me floundering in my own pond of sin. The Eagle had taken off to his eyrie and the Pelican to his nest, and the croaking of the frogs reached me whilst I tried to cover myself with the green moss, but even this slipped and I was left bare. I was again in the world of small rule and petty praise, the wordy world of the spoken prayer, the misshapen world of bent bodies, but He did not come.

When the craving did not go, when the world of people had become a poison, then I knew I had been overcome by the drug.

Once I had seen an alcoholic carted away, and now at last I understood the pitiful longing in his eyes. They had not taken me away, for they had not seen the devil hidden in the spaciousness of my mind. The mind was still my stronghold, no one could probe there, no one could discover him sleeping like a slug on the tendrils of my nerves.

What frightened me most was the idea of life without my chosen pain. I knew I would begin to feel again, once out of the desert I would feel heat and cold, pleasure and pain. How would I endure it when it came? How could I bear to feel again? I would remember the past pains and pleasures of the old world which now were no longer part of my existence. I did not want back my old life of emotions. I cried out for my Protector and for a cover under which to hide, but there was none. They had hunted me early in the day and I had fled from the covert and was now exposed to their cry of triumph, the hounds were upon me and the hunters followed; and He had gone, asleep like a Lover when needed most after the fury, when the pain of solitude permeates the body, and the embracing arm is the only comfort.

> *Strangers have sought after my soul and*
> *They have not set God before their eyes.*
> *God is my helper and the Lord my Protector.*

Yet they could not continue, these horrible wonderings and terrible dreads, these fantasies. I knew it was only in the reality of order and orderliness that I would recover. When the white whip had no longer caused me to feel I knew the sign like a leper. For the lepers the real death had begun when the feeling had stopped. I knew too that to be the crucifier and the crucified was difficult. If Christ had had to administer His own scourging could He have borne it? Could He have faced the ascending cord every week, could He have accepted the anticipation? Could He have crouched under the wheel as it grinded around each week? I did not know. At this time all was confusion, pain and scruple. Every thought, every word, was scrutinised and scoured until speech became impossible and human comprehension inadequate. But my strength remained and I did not die, and the premature desert trial went and I found myself again in the void loneliness.

5

AS THE desert life ended the season of Advent approached. In preparation for His coming the convent took on the glow of expected life and was caught up in the warmth of motherhood. The liturgy now chanted in the grey chapel was full of hope; darkness was giving place to light, fear to hope. The church, like the mother, had been waiting for eight months now, and full of impatience called on Him to come. The last month of preparation was busy with desire. The seasons of empty hopelessness had passed and the glow touched everything, the expected sun in the mid-winter affected us all. Even the little mother in the statue smiled mysteriously as the month drew on. I called on Him to come, not this time in the rounded bread, but as the white circled child of Christmas.

This season had always enchanted me with its tale of wise men and timid shepherds, and angels who dropped from heaven with surprise and joy. Voices in the air and hope in the heavens; all of these I anticipated with a childlike fervour and fever.

I envied the warm motherhood Mary who, in virginity, had obtained the longed for of nations—the birth of a child and the God. Mostly it was the child that fascinated me. I wondered if the birth, like the conception, would be painless. Would He in His eagerness to greet the world come with facility like the grape from the vine, or would He tear the unaccustomed womb of the fragile woman? This happening of birth with its painful onslaught worried me often. Had God been unable to think of less painful methods? Had He really thought that pain so suffered made a bond with the child? Was it the pain or the child that made the bond?

Sometimes I imagined the silken child coming with soft warm helping movements. Then, I was not sorry for the little Mother who carried the stock of Jesse, she looked so warm and full in the flushed statues. As a woman I envied her her rounded belly of soft hope, and subsequent pain. It was a pain of union, of connection, severed indeed in the last hours of that Christmas Day. But at least there had been the union, the neediness of motherhood had encompassed Mary as it would never us. Mary had had the two worlds, and had stood there, with ox and ass, flushed with her dual accomplishment. I felt myself empty and bare like the Advent altar, without flower, without colour. I waited for the coming, my birth by proxy, joying in the accomplishment of the other Virgin who retained her smile in the cold, hard chapel.

With the waiting for the silvered baby of Christmas I began to feel the emptiness of my body. I wanted no more than Mary, I wanted no more than my right—the power to use my body, the power to feel the warmth of life from its beginning. From the stem of creation I wanted a shoot. There was no baby, there would be no flowing over from the breasts—they would be dry, as though in the desert, from the excessive heat. I was needed by no one, not even Christ. In His severance from Heaven He had picked His

43

woman, and soon she would croon Him to sleep amidst the heavy breath and sweetness of the patient animals in the stable. Even now I envied the animals their close proximity. I wondered about them. Why, of all the patient animals, were they so privileged?

The Christmas season came again, full of mystery, bringing the soft rounded body of a Virgin to a wondering world of biologists.

When I returned to the Novitiate room the statue of the Mater Dolorosa waited for me. I looked again at the mother, wrenched apart in her sorrow, with the baby of Christmas wracked before her. I again was sorry for her, she who had been betrayed by the Christmas song. Many a mother had had this experience—the rounded baby changing to criminal proportions before she had realised he was a man. So too with Mary who had awaited Him with warmth and longing. How many times, I thought, did she want to take Him in her arms and lull Him to sleep and keep the peepers at bay—the onlookers who had not known the Christmas Son? There was no keeping them at bay—now she knew this, the mother of sorrows, the mother of warmed flesh, of hopefulness. No longer did I envy her; the warm breasted virgin had paid her price, the baby was no more, there was no more crooning or rocking, only the death wailing over the pale bruised body that could no longer lift its head or touch the loving breast.

As I sat making the holly garland of Christmas I did not envy. The early Christmas joy was moving to the back of my mind, and the crucified Christ had taken His place.

"Little Baby of Bethlehem be comforted. They cannot overcome you completely, we are with you now, and then."

How I would have comforted Him if He were here now. If only I could touch Him, if only He had not become such

44

a thing of the spirit. How easy for Mary to take Him, the little wondersome baby, and croon Him to peace.

With the opening of Mary's womb the clouds would move apart and He would come, and we would welcome Him, here in this decorated room. The holly with its green hopefulness glistened on the wall, but the thorns of the garland pricked our hands as we worked in the long room.

In honour of the Feast that was so soon to come there was a special recreation. We talked and worked with a new and gayer freedom and the feeling of Christmas was everywhere. We broke off into small groups with those who were the most congenial to us, and the old restrictions and regulations were passed over for that day.

Sister Imelda and Sisters Catherine, Ursula, Anthony and I worked together and we thought about our homes and our families. Even scowling Catherine had somehow brightened her face for the Feast, and the sniff that was always there did not any longer seem disdainful, but helped to emphasise the new atmosphere.

"It's like a new world." Imelda said.

"The reality of Christmas is one thing one never gets at home." Catherine remarked.

"At home we did." Ursula said shyly.

I could see her thinking back to the Irish Christmases that were holy and merry in the true sense. They were family occasions those Christmases, and she was momentarily wistful.

"At home we had nothing but continual confusion until Boxing Day." I was saying this more to the holly than to the group. I was seeing again the kitchen suffused with the trappings of Christmas—half-finished parcels for the neighbours, and then on Christmas Day the untidy confusion of opened gifts and half-eaten meals.

45

Anthony smiled at me. She also came from a family where tidiness had not been the most striking feature of their every-day life.

"Did you get your letters off home?"

I was surprised to find her speaking so directly to me when so many of the group were there.

I told her I had managed most of them but couldn't find much to say. In a way I was relieved to learn she had experienced similar difficulty.

During the period of Advent one was not allowed to receive or to write letters. During that time I had wanted again and again to write. When letter-writing permission had been granted I had been delighted. It was only later that I found that I could think of very little to write. So little was happening, and what had happened seemed to me to be of little interest to my family.

"It's always the same," Anthony remarked. "I find if you want something too much, when the opportunity comes the desire seems to leave you."

Her gentle voice sounded puzzled, and I was sorry I could not say something to console her, but I was afraid to say much in case I unwittingly embarrassed her.

We went on making the garland and made some remark that the thorns of the Passion were not far off.

"The berries are like blood," I said, and was sorry as soon as the words were spoken. She looked up from the garland.

"Yes, we can really never forget it. There is no Feast when the Passion can be completely forgotten. He was anticipating His death as soon as He came into life. He lived each moment of His life in every moment, so all the joys and sorrows were intermingled. Like us He had to live

46

centred on the future and live His life buoyed up on the dream of the tomorrow."

One of the others broke into the conversation and teased us about a serious theological treatise. We continued the making of the garlands and listened to the others as they talked. Their talk was more in keeping with the Feast. Sister Ursula was telling us that the rules of Christmas were much less strict and Sister Catherine was brightening up, her complexion was warmer and she was less tense than I had ever seen her.

"A future Aquinas." This was directed to me. I felt self-conscious for a moment and concentrated on the garland.

"Not me," I said, "I don't need a piece of the table cut away."

She laughed out loud and trailed a section of the holly along the room and stood on a chair and placed the garland along the wall.

"Is it straight?" She was balancing precariously on the edge of the chair, and as she turned to adjust the garland to our directions her foot slipped and the chair capsized beneath her. We all laughed noisily.

Immediately a small bell tinkled and the voice of the Novice Mistress came out clearly above the chatter that was so suddenly silenced.

"This recreation is not allowed to become a children's party. Don't forget where you are and the reason for this feast. Recreation may now be resumed."

We tried to talk again, but the joy had suddenly gone out of the night and it was difficult to pretend that nothing had happened. I wondered if, like me, they suddenly felt lonely.

We were lonely, all of us, in this Christmas of birth, in

47

this season of begetting. We were contributing nothing to this mangered season of pain. We were the animals, the beasts of burden, the unwanted for Him who had come to His own and had been rejected from the start. In the end they had twisted Him around the tree and nailed Him like a poster on to the board.

But whether with pleasure or pain I knew that the season would come, that the birth so long awaited would come as always, as though there had not been long preparation. He would come to us, not in a painful labour, but in the astonishing peace of Christmas Mass. At midnight the bells would ring and He would come like a page boy to their calling, and we would greet Him, a new born baby, with bowed head and genuflected knee. We could not take Him in our arms for He was still in the bread, but we would remember Him tonight, making the journey through the womb, His first movements in the Sea of Blood, the Child of Blood, of the Sword, of the Parent Separation. He had come to divide us all, family and friend, foe and ally, and finally He would take His rest in us. His escape from the depths of a woman's body would be short-lived, for we would soon take Him again and in the cubicled peace of sleep, and rock Him to rest. I would try, as I had tried many times before as a child, not to sleep in these early sacred hours, so that the guest would not be alone—He whom I had received often before, had carelessly swallowed in the early hours of the morning, had now become my child.

I came out of this reverie to see a young novice whom I had not seen since one of the early recreations. She came into the room with the Infirmarian, who guided her gently by the arm. I noticed at once the change in her pallor and the flushed look in her face. She was a girl of about twenty years and I remembered her at once as the Sister Angela. I had not known that she was ill; she had been taken ill only a few weeks after my arrival, and as I had not known her well I had not noticed her absence. The older novices knew her and greeted her immediately. They were delighted to see her and made room for her. She had the curious quality that ill people do have from time to time. It was as though everything was just out of her reach. She was too weak to stretch for anything at all, and had thus established a fragile contact with those around her. She sat far from me and was made comfortable with the only cushion in the room. She had a small piece of embroidery in her hand and as soon as she sat down started to sew.

"Are you better now, Sister?" someone asked.

"Almost completely." She rested her back against the cushions and smiled. She seemed glad to be back. It might have been any feast that we were celebrating, but the flushed colouring and the air of fragility made her life more in keeping with the penetential season, but there was nothing morbid or exaggerated about her. She obviously wanted to lose herself in the group. She was hiding the truth from herself as she covered herself with the companionship that was so readily offered when she came into the room.

I didn't know then what was the matter with her. I remembered vaguely some discussion between the Mistress of Novices and the local doctor. They had been walking along the corridor one day when I had been cleaning. He had said, "It is blessedly rare in young women." The Novice Mistress had muttered something like, "But not rare enough."

I wondered now if that conversation had referred to

Sister Angela. I did not know and would never have asked. It was not possible for a novice to ask anything about another that was of a personal nature. From time to time one novice or another went home for sickness or other reasons, but we were never told their reasons, or indeed that they had gone. They were just not there any more. It was like a slaughter at a prisoner of war camp. The loss was swift and unexpected and no explanation was ever given. The novices were strictly bound to keep any mention of their going from each other, and this was a rule that was never broken.

I wondered about Sister Angela. I noticed that the Novice Mistress was very gentle with her and never reprimanded her in any way. I think that she admired her, or maybe it was that she felt protective towards her. When Sister Angela had come into the room she had said to her, "I am so glad you could come down for Christmas. There mustn't be too much excitement. Tell me if you get tired."

"I'm always tired." She said this not as a complaint but as a truth she felt forced to confess.

"If I need to go back to bed I will let you know."

As she said this I wondered what it was like to be ill in the convent for a long time. The days must have been endless. There was no one to talk to and nothing to do except pray. This is one of the most fatiguing occupations that a sick person could undertake. She must have felt wretchedly lonely in the little narrow cubicle, without any conversation, without even the sight of the other novices. I can never recall that she mentioned this fact, but it must have been so.

The recreation carried on as before and we finished making the decorations for the next day. When the bell rang at nine o'clock we began the vigil that would end with the midnight Mass.

I went into the chapel knowing that in the crumpled sleepiness of the early morning I would caress Him, in the silence of my bed I would nurse Him, in my fatigued body He would have His sleep. I would open the gates and let Him in, the Mighty and the Strong and the rounded silken Baby of Christmas.

> *Thou art my Son, the Lord's word came to me.*
> *I have begotten Thee this day.*
> *What means this turmoil among the nations?*
> *Why do the people cherish vain dreams?*

When the morning came He had gone like a dream miscarried in the daylight, and again I was sad and empty, suffering the depression of a birth. I joined the other proxied mothers but could see no change. The strange new meats at the Christmas breakfast reminded me of my loss and I wanted Him back. I could not celebrate His absence. He had slipped away in the early hours, not like a warm baby, but like a wary lover. The miracle had passed on, and I was left to spend my Christmas in a lettered world of parcelled remembrance. The world had remembered me, letters from foreign people with known addresses were waiting for me, and I joined others who had returned to see in the words a life that no longer knew them. They waited, these young women, no longer silent, but eager with the youth of Christmas, for the glimpse of past childhood and known affection. Fathers and mothers reduced to the written word paraded around the room. Linked with loved brothers and sisters they streamed like so many decorations.

I could feel them entangling me, choking me with their affection and memories. Did they still really know me? Had they been here would they have known me after the birth? I could not tell, they were alien to me now. The joking brothers, the careful sisters, the wise mothers and the loving fathers were dead for us. They did not know the desert, they did not understand the birth, they did not comprehend the separation. If they came now I was sure I would be embarrassed. I had watched the others go to the "Parlour" and had seen their return. The mystified loneliness on their faces had told me—they could not understand—and bereft parents with greying separation wandered homeward down the little garden paths, wistfully looking back at the convent that had enveloped their child. The moment of their passion was enclosed in the stone; a prisoner from their affection, a stranger to their home.

On this day of glory, on this paradisal feast, I felt no longer that the silence was a burden. Since I had left the desert I had considered their silence a cover, a hide-out. Today there was no cover, the ceaseless chatter worried me as had the first day's silence. Now I could feel the companionship grating and the desire for refuge mounting. There was no corner of my world that did not celebrate this day. I wondered about the old nuns who walked with the secret look of belonging. Did they regret the Birth, the passing of time, the empty future of Christmases without a son?

As the day passed with games and feasts, and parcels and greetings, the longing for a child began to be borne in upon me. I could feel a mounting hatred for the doe-eyed Virgin who had fooled them all. Miracle or design she had had her child. They could scorn her in the market places, in the squares, in the streets and villages, the towns and the cities of the world, they could question her virginity, but they could not question her firm bodied Baby. She had Him against all, she was not alone, not empty and pathetic, not following a star, a path of ruled observance. She had instead the warm body to feed, the tiny lips to brush with her virginal lips, a warm stretched lap on which to rock the crooning king. The empty virgins who sat around like jugs waiting to be filled with the wine could see no hope of so warmed a future. The wedding and the changing of the watered wine had only been symbolic, I thought. The water changed into wine when the virgin was changed into a mother, when the empty vessel was full, when the vacant knees were filled, not with the hard board of prayer, but the kicking baby.

Despite the disturbed longings with which the Feast had filled me there were many companions. We sat around and talked and re-read our letters. The small home gifts lay around the tables and the lockers in the Novitiate bulged with the wrappings of the small presents. It was really a family feast, a glorious day for the mothers and small children. There seemed to be something incongruous in the celebration.

Sister Bernadette and Sister Ursula were resting on chairs near to where I was sitting. Sister Bernadette was holding up a small statue of St. Paul, a gift from her family. He was a saint for whom she had great admiration, and I suddenly realised that the statue was a symbol of the life she would lead. St. Paul had left behind him a lesson of discipline and denial which she understood and favoured. Strangely enough it was Sister Ursula who began the controversial conversation. She did not intend it to be so, but it was a discussion I was happy to join. She picked up the crude statue and looked at it carefully.

"He looks quite pleasant. Not at all like a misogynist."

"He needed someone to love him," I said.

"He would have despised any love except that of God. He was completely devoted to God, and all earthly things were abhorrent to him." Sister Bernadette had said this as though she were reading from some ancient text. I was immediately and irrationally irritated by her.

"He completely misunderstood Christ's teaching. It was he and not Christ who made marriage a second-class vocation. If he had been at Cana he might have thought differently," I said.

She chose to ignore my remark and it was Sister Ursula who broke the silence. It was unlike her to enter into an argument. Perhaps she was drunk with the Christmas festivities.

"The idea he had of marriage has haunted the Church ever since. Heloise and Abelard were forced because of this idea into a world of cold stone."

"Yes, they had wanted each other as the fire, the flame. Because of the kind of doctrine St. Paul proposed, the church ruled them out for a life of separation and hopelessness. They put up with this cruel division and had to fret out the remainder of their lives in surrender to the whim of the monastery of their choice. I have never fully understood the right and the wrong of this question." For me this was the longest speech I had ever made in front of Sister Bernadette, and she did not answer me. Very quietly she picked up the statue and walked away.

"Christmas is a time when one feels that some of the penances of the Church should be questioned." I wasn't sure whether Sister Ursula said this to comfort me or whether I had deeply disturbed her usual placidity. I felt

54

uncomfortable and was glad when the recreation period was finished by the ringing of the Benediction bell.

The Christmas Day was broken for the ceremonial of the Benediction. The Eastern quality of this Blessing never failed to stir me. The priest, a magi'd figure robed in a glorious garment of gold came in, a wise man bearing the frankincense. The altar was alight with candles and the joy of the Christmas flowers. The Bambino, placed at the foot of the altar, smiled out a birthday smile on all, and gave no heed to the ceremony. He was oblivious to their placing Him in the gold monstrance and blessing the air with the jewelled vessel whilst the black heads bowed below. The curled straw of the mangered box twined around the toes, and the world looked on. The scent of the incense arose in the chapel with the fragrance of a prayer, and the hymns with their joyous welcome seemed to float through the roof, up past the seagulls, and into the heavens, to the God who had brought them here. They prayed in gratitude for the salvation that had come, but the Bambino in the statuette still smiled, and caught the stray straws, like wandering souls, safe in between the dimpled feet.

Mary, blushing in the light of the Sanctuary, welcomed the shepherds while Joseph, in eunuched happiness, looked on with wistful love. Joseph had grouped himself near the animals so that the onlookers might not think he touched the virgin whom he so protected. He stood firm by, this man of wood, this protector in a world of finger pointers. Yet it seemed that even in the crib he dared not approach, but stood by the entrance like a storm door against the cold night. Did he love her as Abelard and Heloise each other? Did he fear to touch the timid virgin and surprise her with this new passion? The carrier of wood, the bearer of the cross, the Christopher to Christ, what did he feel standing there in an unknownness that had never before been known and never since surpassed?

So it had come again, the season of enchantment and warmth. Suddenly, and without warning, I thought again of Peter. There was nothing to remind me of him, I had not thought of him since that far off night when I had seen the statue of the Mater Dolorosa. When the option of sleep or late conversation was given I went out of the room that had suddenly become oppressive. I tried not to think of Peter, or to see him in my mind, but it was impossible. I longed for comfort, for the warmth of a bodied reality, the kindness of a hand stroking my head. I knew he could not come, could not and would not. I had asked this of him before I came away, and now I regretted my decision. Even as I regretted, I knew it would not have been possible. I had chosen my way of life and there were no half measures. If one chose a life of dedication to God one had chosen, and there was no going back.

There was nothing for me. I went, alone, to the cubicled sleeping place, whispering the Advent hymns, the canticles of Christmas, the song of despair. I had come at last to realise the strangeness of this new world.

I drifted into sleep and wished for a moment for the past mothered-Christmas, the day of the familied warmth. I wanted them so much, the family of no ideals, the family filled now with wine and little Christmas. Did they want me? Did they think of me in the land of the bare gulls in upward movement? Everything moved away towards the heavens. The sky, like a magnet, took all in the claws of tomorrow. The sky had no thought for the day. In the confusion of its many clouds it hid with the million others this day that had been buoyed on a dream and sunk.

6

DESPITE THESE longings of the Christmas Day the joyful days that followed the feast were a relaxation for all in the house. The feeling of peace was everywhere. The garden was silent and neglected because the cold weather had come, and when I walked there again the bare whiteness surprised me. Now it was like a new kingdom for me and I loved the sparsity. I drew in the air and felt happy as I moved. I missed the gulls, who had scarcely been seen, though some huddled between the rocks, shivering and forlorn.

They cried rarely these days, and I missed them when I walked in the night. I thought of them as my friends and wanted their joyful return.

This day was the feast of the Circumcision of the Baby. This was the day when the wooden carpenter and Mary had brought the swaddled king to the Temple and called Him by His name—the name that would never be forgotten. This day the persecution of the Jews had begun. The Jews had not understood the whimpering bundle as it was carried carefully to the Temple. For a moment I saw Joseph and Mary as the instigators of the Fuhrers. Had they left the Baby quietly at home there would have been

57

none of the criminal confusion that had started the death for Christ and the continual running for the Jews. Did they know, these two, that they were for ever causing the Jewish families to run, clutching their moneybags, from place to place like homeless birds? I understood their monied existence, these unloved people, they who sought for refuge and found it under a pile of coins silvered by the Christian hand. Had He seen too the many in the camps of the past atrocity? Had the Bundled Baby waved His hand in happy sanction to their lot? His people, His chosen from all time, did He know, this tiny One?

In the doctrine I had found the answer I did not want to hear. He had known all from the beginning. From the first mistake He had known. From the evil moment of the first mother He had seen it all, and had left them, Jew and Gentile, to their lot.

They had been, at first, the Jewish people, the most famous of all time, the loved of God, the Desired of Nations, the ancestors of Christ. The child had seen it all, and yet had thrown them each, as coldly as the Hitlered regime, into the gas chamber—had smothered the raven-haired mothers in the consuming fire. Had they always to pay, I wondered, would not one life suffice, was the killing of Christ so great it might never be undone, was the mistake so great they could not be forgiven, were they all Judases, had they all thrown the bread out to the ravaging wolves who were hungry for carnage? Could they not be forgiven? Were they to go always to the ends of the earth, unwanted and despised, the least among men?

As I thought of this they passed before me, Hitler, Goebbels, Goering, Eichmann and Christ—He with His people driven cringing before Him in the little garden where I walked. Here they moved for me, the recipients

58

of the generations of blood. It seemed there was no Christianity without Judaism, no Judaism without Christianity. Christ's followers had refused to exonerate the Jews, generation after generation? Had they not, all of them, kept for ever, under the pretence of love of God, the curse of Christ on the Jews? Had they not stood by whilst six million of them were burnt, scourged, gassed, and tortured to death? They sent them back to Christ with the marks of Christianity on their backs, the scars that were made by His followers. Could He face them when they came, the little groups of shrivelled people, His descendants that had been suffering for Him? What excuse did He offer to them? Did He relent?

There was no forgiveness for the Jews. They had been punished cruelly and continually in the name of Christ who had grown so mysteriously cold in the garden, and had left me, shivering and wondering, frightened at such anger. They had not recognised the pen portrait in the Bible. They had not known the king, and they had suffered rejection and loneliness, and had clasped at their money bags, their only security, ever since.

Sometimes it seemed to me there could be no satisfying Christ. His own terrible virtue made Him unassailable. The Jews were repugnant to Him perhaps, He who was so perfect that He could not forgive. Was there ever any worse sin, I wondered, than the revenge on the generations that followed? Was there any worse sin than the inability to forgive? He could not forgive them, and His followers ensured they paid for every nail in His hands and every wound in His body with their very blood.

I thought again then on the book of Ruth whose name through baptism I bore.

And Naomi said unto Ruth her daughter in law, "It is good my daughter, that thou go out with his maidens, that they meet not in any other field." So she kept fast by the maidens of Boaz to glean unto the end of barley harvest and of wheat harvest. . . .

When would it be, this new harvest? I thought. When would the wheat be gathered; when could I leave the fields and shut out for ever these Christian reapers, these gleaners with the blood on their hands? Could I ever wash away the blood of the Jews? Could I ever be anointed so that the world would know I did not condemn them, these Jews, formerly so loved and now cast out? The happiness they had sought now seemed to have gone for ever out of the world. When He had died, when the benighted Jews twisted Him around the tree, He had taken happiness with Him. Was it to punish humanity that He took all with Him, or was it that when God went from the world happiness went as a matter of course? Did they get closer to Heaven than I, the Jews in their wanderings and the drunks in their ecstasy? I hoped so. I tried to answer all these questions but there was no possibility of comprehension in this world of trickery.

He had cheated me often, this little God who had wrapped the straw around Him in his mangered existence. Was He a God of Love or a whipped-up Trapper who liked all to His taste? Did He really think of them here? Did He really think of them as they wandered about without Him? Did He stay at the judgement seat every minute waiting for the sinners to appear so that He might cast them out for ever into the torments of Hell?

He who was the begetter of all had begun their lives with full knowledge of what was to come. Did He want them to fail? And, if not, why did He not keep the failures in the silence of non-existence? The doctrine of the Free Will was not enough for me. If he wanted us to cope He should only have made people who could understand Him. Why did He perplex us?

Hell was a certainty. I had thought on this often. In our human comprehension we had failed to understand the reality. The image had haunted Christianity since He had divided the world into the sheep and the goats. He had threatened the herd with this incredible extinction. Was the fabled fire the true pain? He had spoken in human terms of this inhuman punishment. Never had humanity experienced pain without respite, never had they considered anything as unending. In the reality of humanity things changed, intense pain brought in its finality death as the release.

Sometimes it seemed that everything that gave humanity pleasure caused God to despise the pleasure and the accepting humanity who enjoyed it. Had His human suffering warped Him? Had He, ever since the Agony, been unable to think of man in terms of anything but suffering? Had the Son affected the Father and Holy Ghost, and encouraged them to cast out for ever the weak? Why had we not all been limboed and crept into the peaceful existence of the unknowing? It would have been safer and easier, and would have been without pain. I had wanted God in His love, but He had appeared to me as my Judge—fair in His judgement. The cruelty of His fairness was evident. Justice, I thought, was a terrifying feature of the Godhead. Had He been less just I might have been better able to comprehend Him. The coldness of this virtue had always been abhorrent to me. His love which had been shown in the Agony had been so strangely mishandled. He had always wanted a return for His love, for His generous act. Century after century He had demanded the flow of priests and monks and nuns. I had answered Him because I had been afraid of what was to come. Like a business director He had sought after returns. Now I had difficulty in comprehending the whole. I had not asked Him to come and had not asked for the Fall, had asked indeed for nothing but oblivion. He had imposed His generosity on me, and arranged all between the Father whom He was, and then sent out the account. Mercilessly the shareholders in His concern were frightened to withhold their return. His reign of terror, so neatly carried out by Christendom, filled me now with horror, and thinking of my lost family huddled in the glow of their own closeness I was again frightened. Would He dismiss them in the Judgement Day for the wrong word, the stolen penny, the out of place love, the warmed temper full of angry words? Was it possible to lose Him in one moment of passion if the appropriate words were not hurtled to the heavens at its completion? I feared for them, the little family of quick movement and tardy repentance. Would He throw them into the pit? I could not bear to see them falling with Satan from the heights to depths for ever. It was the eternity of the punishment that harassed me. For the moment of pleasure snatched in the world of twined pain could they not be brought back in time?

7

THE SEASON of Christmas passed, and the fragile cycle of the enclosed women battened through the long winter months against the all surrounding rigidity. The cold weather came into the land already frozen and wanting the spring that seemed so far away. In the darkness of the morning the cycle began and ended with the closed darkness of the night.

For the novices the monastic routine began to gather its full strength. The fault speaking and the rigid penance were more strictly observed as the season of Lent began to draw in. The obsession with the details of the Noviceship rule accentuated the preliminary waiting of the Lenten season. The careful observance of the rule, and the continual turning of the eye to the ground were becoming for me more natural and less difficult. The world seemed far away with its temptation and lures, and I settled into the slow numbing sensation of the organised existence.

The routine of the prayerful world, divided by work and sleep, continued to exhaust us all, though, at the same time, giving us a purpose for being.

Unexpectedly, Sister Catherine and I were sent over to help in the boarding school. The building lay across the garden from the Novitiate, and looked cosier even from the outside. The nun who usually prepared the linen was ill, and our work was merely the arranging of sheets and pillow-cases for the bedrooms. It was a big job, and we were expected to remain there for the greater part of the day. For this reason we were given permission to speak, partly because we would miss our usual recreation period, and partly because the task itself required us to speak to each other.

I was glad to have an opportunity to speak to Sister Catherine who had seemed more moody than usual. We walked up the stairs silently, only the large beads which we wore attached to the cincture rattled and swished as we moved along and into the room.

"What a spot of luck!" she said, disregarding the unwritten rule of "correct" speech.

"How do you mean?" I said as I unfolded an enormous sheet and looked feverishly for the name tag. The sheet was very large, and at that moment I thought of luck as something that was always passing me by. She smiled into a pillow case.

"Here it is." She pulled out a name tag as though it were a kitten she had caught by the scruff of the neck. "They should be told to put their names on the outside. It would save time if nothing else."

I was still entangled in the enormous sheet and felt quite incapable of assessing which side was the outside. There was no name tag on either side of the four corners. I dropped exhausted into a chair that was nearby.

"Tired already?"

"I was tired before I came."

I watched her. She was a neat methodical worker and would have done the work for us both without any complaint. She was piling up the sheets and the pillow cases.

"Dormitory One complete. There must be twins in Dormitory Two, unless Flanagan has four sheets."

I remembered the twins, four-year-olds, whose parents were abroad.

"That's right," I said. "There are twins in Number Two. They're only four."

"Four! What an age to send children away to school."

"They could do worse than here." I believed this. The school was reasonable. The nuns were kind to the children, and probably cared more for them than did their parents.

"Take the sheets for Three and I'll do Four and Five." Sister Catherine was twice as quick as I was and I agreed. I was glad that she had taken the position of leader. Leadership in the convent was determined not by age but by years of entry. If one nun was one day longer in the convent than another she was senior to her. According to this regulation I was senior to Sister Catherine by one week. This was a privilege I was more than willing to hand over.

"Brown, two; Green, two; Robinson, two; Samuels, two; Ryan, one—where is it?"

"What?" I asked.

"Ryan has only one sheet."

"There must be another somewhere."

She had started to sing a gloomy song about a winding sheet without realising I could hear her.

"You had better stop that," I said. "The nuns are along the corridor."

"Got it," came the reply.

One soul saved for a time from the winding sheet, I thought.

Sister Catherine was humming the tune of the winding

song, and I thought, for the first time, that she was a personality, and not just a nameless blackness.

"I never knew you could sing."

"Is that what you thought it was?"

She seemed to have become so much brighter I couldn't believe it was the same person who had seemed so sullen at recreation the previous night. I knew then what I had missed. During the months we had been there we had all of us tried to hide our real character. We ate when everyone was hungry, and were penitential together. There had seemed to me little room for the person, the character to develop.

We worked all that day and I was warmed with the companionship. I told her my greatest desire was to teach in the school.

"I'm not qualified like you, but I love children."

She listened and said nothing. I knew she was happy and had enjoyed the change from the Novitiate.

Two days later the Novice Mistress sent for me.

"They are short-staffed over in the Junior school. I would like you to go over and help them out."

Sister Catherine must have told her what I had said. The Novice Mistress was like many people who have never been to a university and set great store by the number of letters one filled in after one's name. It must have been the letters that lent weight to Sister Catherine's argument.

Lent would begin in a few weeks, and I knew I would have to return to the Novitiate as soon as the penitential season began.

I went over to the boarding school in the middle of the week. The children seemed to sit as though they were just images of life. They sat at the pallid desks that were deaf to their thoughts. They carved the names of their friends on to the lids so that the wood might spring to life as they looked at it in the early morning. I felt for them, these little children of the rich, as they sat isolated with their money in the cold convent of the rich boarding school. They waited, each child, for the next item to cast off the boredom of the present. Whether rich or poor they needed their parents, I thought.

In the early morning hours the children passed me in polite arrival in the classroom. They absorbed into their land of hope and joy the strange symbols that were thrust upon them. They incorporated all for the sake of peace. I taught them adult values which they played with in their hours of freedom. I saw them often in the free hours imitating me in the garden. They taught each other with the same emphasis and gestures, little nuns in the in-between land of the child.

I was watching them one day at the recreation period and listening to them. Two small girls were playing at the edge of the lawn. They were bouncing a ball with their hands and counting the number of bounces. Snatches of their conversation came across the path.

"My father's better than yours."

"Why is he?"

"He's a doctor."

"So's mine."

"My father's a better doctor than yours."

"He's not."

"I said he is. He's the doctor to a lot of famous people."

"My father's the doctor to a prince."

"My father goes to Buckingham Palace."

To this superlative the little girl could not reply. There seemed to her nothing bigger and better than Buckingham Palace, and she bounced the ball hard. In the ferocity of the stroke the ball eluded her on the second bounce, and she ran after it quickly, glad of the excuse to leave the breaker of images. Heroes and heroines crumble quickly in the hands of small children.

The ball rolled on to the gate and she followed it sturdily. She stayed at the gate and looked down the road, as though she were hoping the road would produce her father. It seemed to her, I thought, that the missing father would jump up at any moment like the cheerful Yo-Yo she sometimes held.

She slowly retraced her steps and jumped the small lined pavement, wishing and promising rewards to herself as she avoided the cracks in the ground, which, although they had been formed by the cruelty of the weather, had taken on for her a magical quality.

Her little companion crossed the path and joined her.

"Let's jump the cracks then."

"The first on the crack takes a whack."

"No, the first on the crack breaks her back," the other corrected.

They hopped along, missing the twists in the ground with great care. They were like little crickets, even their voices, which were further away now, seemed to chirp out that they were really alive. The enmity that had seemed as though it might flourish had disappeared completely. Their wishes and their desires depended on the crack in the ground. The return of their parents, the serving of their favourite meal, their whole existence depended on the favour of the garden gods. Did they understand the reality of the faith under which they were being bullied into observance? Did they, these little white groups, understand the early morning call to the chapelled Mass of the sixth hour? They could not possibly understand. Their whole lives were based around the Christmas tree and the favour of the good fairy. They could not comprehend gods who died and suffered again and again in the early hours. They were simple in their wishes these small children of the rich families.

I rang the bell for the end of recreation and they clustered into their lines. They were not eager to get back to the classroom, but they enjoyed the huddled quality of the line-standing. It was a good chance to push and to chatter. The noise gradually died away except for the muffled whispering of the very brave. They knew that as soon as complete silence was restored they would be sent into the building, and this fate was kept at a distance for as long as it was possible to do so without much repercussion.

They were accustomed to such remarks as, "I will not tell you again to stand quietly, and that means complete silence." They heard this kind of command every day and it was this that ended the recreation period. They were used to this, and they waited for it as the last signal that their freedom was ended for another hour.

The hours in the classroom were devoted to inculcating the adult values and ideals. Their small minds were beaten into the realisation of the present and its demands. They were there to be taught, and since the opportunity for diversions were few, they learnt as much as their minds could absorb. The limitation of the minds of children came to me very strongly during one lesson.

They used what was then considered a modern mathematics book. The stages of mathematics were clearly set out. The end section of the text was concerned with unbelievable excursions into the mysteries of long division. One child, after a monumental effort at this division, brought out the book with an air of triumph and a badly concealed smugness.

"I've finished."

"Completely?"

"Yes, the whole book."

"You must have a new book tomorrow." As I said this I removed an unsightly ruler from the sleeve of a baggy jersey in the front row.

"But what else is there to do? I thought long division was the end of sums."

"It's the end of the book but not the end of sums."

"What other kinds of sums are there?"

"Pounds, shillings and pence sums."

"Do you divide pounds, shillings and pence sums?"

"Sometimes."

"Is it the end of sums when you've done that?"

"No."

Someone had once told me that there was a point where mathematics and philosophy joined and when that point was reached it was difficult to separate the two. I was not sure if this were true (I'm still not sure), but I could see the conversation was about to take a philosophical turn. I began to feel I would end up by trying to explain infinity.

"When is it the end of sums?"

"Not for a long time yet."

"How long?"

"As long as you're in this school."

"How many holiday times will that be?"

I had to stop the conversation to catch a rubber in hasty transit across the room. I put it in my pocket and looked as though I hadn't seen it at all.

"How long is it to the holidays now?"

"Would you like to help me by tidying that cupboard?"

70

I had noticed that children in the early years took it as a mark of special favour if they were asked to do some small job. She accepted it as a reward for her early completion of the book and sank down by the door of the cupboard, and looked at the jumbled books with the air of a librarian looking at rare manuscripts. I left her to the task and walked around the room.

Some of the note-books looked weary. They curled up, and the numbers seemed to gyrate around the pages without any order. There had been in many cases liberal and unskilful use of the rubber, and the ugliness of this was further accentuated by the implanting of traces of glue and plasticine. On the whole they were not the most intelligent children I have ever known, but they were some of the most likeable, and I missed them when the term of teaching ended.

The cold weather came unexpectedly that year. The snow that came from whatever it was that organised the adult life, dropped, giving them a new existence and a miracle of a new world where the adult foot had not yet come, where the prints of pained life had not started to walk. They ran to build new fathers out of the cold snow, carving their images with raw hands and warm minds. The caressed fathers stood for hours in the playground, strangers in the land, but known to combine the virtues of the childish dream—strong and tall, cosy and fat, cigar-smoking kings in a world of green. They stood in the garden listening to the clapping hands of the little gods who felt, for the first time, their power as creators that would come again to make the images, the next time like themselves.

Mittened in their work they started in and out, forgetful of the cold sleepiness of the morning and the boring kindness of the classroom. They were there, happy in the waiting for the darkness to come so that they might creep with the newly made fathers into the warm bedded life of dreams.

Again there was the strange complexity for me as I watched the children make the father. Had it been so with humanity that they had built a rounded God out of the white bread?

After the creation they ran to the wall for the leg swinging routine that came after every accomplishment. They watched the snowman, captive in the garden, unable to move without their permission, unable to disappear whilst the coldness remained. I had watched one night a bereft child sidle along this very wall to kiss the image that stood for all in the shadow of the hedge. The child had looked surprised as she turned from his cigar-smoking mouth, amazed at the coldness of the smoke that seemed to come. She had wanted little out of her rich world, just the warm mouth of her invisible father who had gone without warning. She had gone back to the dormitoried groups without a word and clutched the prominent toy that had lain alone all during the day. The beheaded golliwog served her purpose for the night.

As long as the snow remained the children were happy. They endured the knowledge that came into the classroom, since the endurance would make time pass more quickly, so they could reach the snow.

But even the snow deserted them in time. The wet slush surrounded the convent as they woke on the third day. I saw them as they passed the fading snowman; their wishes melted in the garden as I held them captive in the classroom where they learnt little, but the lesson of the passing came strongly with the morning thaw.

They absorbed the pain as they bent in the garden and

touched the dark water that promised them little. They had autonomy no longer. Their position of creator was usurped by the wind and the rain, and they went back to their memoried world of dreams, waiting for the next snow or the next holiday that might produce their parents from the faraway land.

It was my occupation to bring them back from the magical seven-year-old world of anticipation. They walked in the gardens, not with knowledge of the past, but with their dreams of the future, always in the child mind so different from the present.

They produced in the playground the little families to which they felt they belonged : the position of the mother or father decided by the drop of a stone or a toss of a penny, or the bounce of a ball. The haphazard "I'm on!" came and went like the seasons, and I noticed above all that they were happy in this arbitrary world of chance. In their ability to accept the present they were superior to me. Their sufferings were less deep because the idea of termination was still their belief. They had not yet learnt about the recurrence of the ills that came and went. When they went they considered that the end; and when they returned they did not think of the return as part of the departed cycle but of a fresh beginning that was. The future was lost for them in the *is*, and the past in the *was* that never became firmly established.

They learnt the mastery of the written word and the justice of the mathematical division that was their life in the little classroom. They drew for themselves the reflections of the child mind and were delighted by the faces that appeared from nowhere on to the canvas and disappeared as they rubbed them into oblivion. They needed this power in the world that forever pushed and organised them.

73

During this time I understood the difference between the adult and the child. For the child all was possibility, the power of the adult was infinite, they asked and it was obtained. For the adult the end of adolescence had come when the limitations of this power were recognised and their hopes were forced into a terrible realisation of the paucity of the human ability. So I saw myself in my sphere of restricted power and limited hope. The strength that I obtained through this realisation carried me through the remaining years in the noviceship.

My term of teaching was shortened by the beginning of the Lenten season, and I was forced to leave the children as they began to recognise themselves and feel their own existence in the new world of the eighth year.

8

I MISSED THEM as I retraced my steps back into the
Novitiate with its strict routine. It was their optimism
I missed most of all. They were always so hopeful that
some change would come about, and that something
wonderful would happen to chase away the sadness of
the present moment. In the rigidity of the ruled life that
followed so fixed a timetable there could be little hope.

When the observance became more severe even the re
membrance of the children became dim. I began to concen-
trate on the Lenten season and the great Easter Feast tha
would rise like a spring in the land of dry penance.

As the days passed the rooms in the Novitiate seemed tc
close down on me. I wanted desperately the freedom of the
garden. The walls surrounded me like oppressive sins I
could not push aside. The Novice Mistress noticed the
depression and was carefully kind.

As I knelt in her room during the advice period I was
impressed by the perceptive quality that she showed.

"It will pass, Sister, and when it does you will forget
that it has ever been. A life of enclosure is in itself a minor
crucifixion, and to endure this and to remain is sometimes
a severe penance in itself."

75

"You are right, Mother," I said, "but at the moment I cannot think about a time when this feeling will not be. It is pressing me down now and I can only think of this. I have tried not to show my discomfort, but one day I will cry out loud and they will think I am mad."

"You are not mad, and they will say nothing of the kind, because you will never give them cause. You have more reserve than you give yourself credit for. When the feeling of closure becomes too great go out on to the top walk in the garden and look down on to the sea. The noise and the movement will free you."

She was right. As I stood in the garden the sad cry of the gulls rose and fell, and I wondered if I would endure the captivity for ever. Even as I stood there I knew that to be caught up in the wounds of Christ and to be twined into Eternity with the ropes that bound Him would be the strong chain that would keep me there.

When I so thought of Him I felt for Him in His suffering here, but truly I had not asked Him to come. Yet had He not come what would there have been? As I asked the many times posed question I saw moving before me a life time of ordinariness without love, and was glad He had come and I had understood Him. It was at moments like this I knew I was not a stranger in the cold land, but that there was but a brief wind needed to blow me into His world, the world that was opened to all who had sought their refuge in Him.

A day or two after my conversation with the Novice Mistress I was surprised by the sudden harsh arrival of the bitter Ash Wednesday ceremonies.

The week at the onset had threatened little. The mornings of that week had begun with the old weariness but had demanded nothing extra. This morning had suddenly thrust once again the old refrain of pain into the routine, just when I was recovering a degree of equilibrium. The interim cycle in the calendar of organised devotion, was suddenly lost.

The darkness of the unexpected morning brought out the psalm loud and clear in the chapel that had been more friendly during the recent weeks than ever before. I had begun to feel this becoming part of me. The prayer surprised me in its strength of the past pain.

> *O God, see how the waters close about me,*
> *Threatening my very life.*

We cried out for mercy in the chapel, black Ninevites of a new age. We circled the railings by the altar, and knelt with submission whilst the priest covered the foreheads of the innocent and guilty alike. The cry of the change of vesture went through the chapel as the ashes were placed on the forehead and the strange annointing took place. We returned dirtied by our sins.

I remembered how, as a child, I had hated this ceremony that had cursed us on this day. Mounting the buses at the well-known places kindly people had told us of the marks on our foreheads. I could hear the voices as I knelt there by the rails.

"You've smudged your face, love."

"Been doing the cleaning then, ducks?"

"Had coal for your breakfast then?"

"Here, give it a rub with this." This remark was accompanied by the presentation of an immaculate paper handkerchief. To have used it would have been the equivalent of recanting at the stake. To refuse seemed churlish, and kneeling on the cold floor I could feel my face warming at the remembrance. The childhood embarrassment had been real and cruel, but I never recanted. Even the remark "Funny little things these convent kids" did not move me. The mark was as singular as the Jewish features, and I was half ashamed and half pleased. Now the disfiguring of the face in the house of accepted disfigurement did not trouble me. I wished only for the waters of cleanliness that moved forever out of my reach on a tide that was all flow, and reluctant to come back to the banks from which it had started. There had been nothing strange for me in the Mass that demanded that not the garments but the "hearts must be torn asunder". It was only the reversal to this new cry that was an agony.

After the procession of nuns had left, the priest annointed the heads of the children who retained, in the early morning hours, their element of innocent surprise, and the uneasy feeling that the neat uniform might suddenly change into sackcloth and ashes. They huddled up together and wondered about the adults who thrust sin upon one so unexpectedly in the early morning hours. They connected sin with classroom negligence and the tempting sweet, or daring disobedience. But to find it here so early in the morning was a shock that required suitable remedy. A little sleep reduced it to its appropriate importance in minds that could take shock in very small quantities.

From the Novitiate bench I saw them fidgeting in the alien greyness of the morning. These small rich children with their crouched gestures in the front benches were a reminder of the Victorian sweeps, whom, no doubt, the ancestors of these very children had sent racing up the chimneys to return with the dust of their trade, the evidence of their sin of impoverishment, on their faces. Clustered in the benches at the front of the chapel the new sweeps sat waiting for the end of the ceremony and the beginning of something else in this environment of early shock.

For me, however, the coldness was beginning again, the outside feeling of the oberver began again to overtake me as I saw the children for whom I cared forced into a ceremony they did not comprehend.

For the children the hour had its merits. They kept the scars on their foreheads during the day, it was a mark of distinction that the "home-bedded friends" would not have. They would enter the schoolroom without these scars of selection. It was here, I thought, the hypocrisy of religion began. We were, all of us, children and adults alike, concerned with the outward form, and were no better than the hypocrites against whom Christ had railed.

The outward form of ceremony was so important in the Church, and indeed in the convent it was all that seemed to matter in these early days. The ability to walk with silent foot and downcast eye, to fold the hands into the inevitable folds, this was all they asked. As the season moved on, however, the penances began to be felt, the rules of silence were more strictly observed, and the novices followed the Lenten fasts. The early morning rising made this more difficult, but the training and the routine soon established them in the pattern. I began to forget the rule of the earlier months and to consider the diet we now had as the usual one for my life. It was neither the silence nor the restricted food that worried me in the end, but the chapel with the mournful purple of the liturgical season.

The custom in the Roman Church of covering the statues had never seemed strange to me before. Now, however, when I spent so many hours of my harsh day in the chapel, the hidden statues filled me with the despair of the season. I wanted back the little Virgin with the child clasped close. The Christ who had stood with His welcoming look was hidden under the poorly dyed purple. There was no majesty there, just the strange stuffiness of unused Godhead. They had hidden Him under the cloth as they had hidden Him under the Tabernacle, away from me when I searched for Him. The early mornings in the chapel seemed gloomier than ever; without the colourful image I was lost in the morning meditations. Even the limited reality of the statues had gone, and I was left to wander in the purple world.

We absorbed, all of us in the Novitiate, the cruel season. We had no letters from our homes and wrote none. The Lenten season brought us the first total separation of our entrance. We wondered often, all of us, about the left families and questioned their well-being in the wordless world. For me this was a painful time. I wanted to communicate and was prevented; like a prisoner I felt the need for parole, but there was none. There was in fact nothing at this time given to help. The time for help had passed in the interim period between Advent and Lent. Now we were faced with the monastic life in its entirety, and in the cruel impersonality of the penitential season we had, this time, to survive without help. This was one of the periods of testing. The senior novices ended this period with their profession and final surrender to the monastic world.

The atmosphere in the Novitiate changed. I could feel this at the recreation periods where the conversation became even more tense. There was started at this time also the special observance. This required us to tell one another our faults and then later to declare them openly.

It repulsed me, this concentration on the tiniest details of the rule. Each of us had a partner for the admonition period, and I was closeted with Sister Bernadette.

"Sister," she said to me one day, "I have watched you during the week, you are untidy and slipshod and seem unable to observe the basic rules of modesty. You know our rule here; the hands are to be joined in a special position and you are supposed to walk on the ball of your foot, not on your heels like a ploughman."

It was my turn then to admonish her. I looked round the cold room for inspiration; I could think of nothing.

"There is nothing that occurs to me just now," I said.

She looked at me strangely and walked away. She was clutching her little stunted notebook and entered something in it as she stood by the window.

It was later that the Novice Mistress sent for me.

"It appears, Sister, that you seek popularity rather than carry out the duties that were given to you."

"What do you mean?" I asked.

I knew what she meant but it gave me time to think. I realised that Sister Bernadette, after the admonition period, went straight to the Mistress. It was a perverted humility that made her go. She had wanted the Mistress to know that no fault had been observed in her, and she wanted to appear distressed that, despite her wickedness, I had not had the strength of character to point out her foibles.

"Had Sister Bernadette no fault?" the Mistress asked.

"Nothing that I had noticed during the week."

But now I know that inside that perfect frame there was corruption of the worst kind. It was the same in whatever walk of life you were. There was always the "creep" who moved with smooth movement that the ordinary man dreaded. I had seen this when I had worked one holiday in a factory; the worker who had run to the forewoman with the news that someone was smoking in the lavatory, or was snatching a kiss behind the bumper packets of produce that were the special offer of the moment.

I lost some of my respect for Sister Bernadette after that. She was dressed in the same habit as I but the difference between us was insurmountable.

The Mistress was intoning some sombre tale of the duty that was incumbent on novices, but I could think of nothing but the shabbiness and the hypocrisy of the whole movement.

I never spoke to Sister Bernadette again. There was no point at which we could meet. She disapproved of me and I feared her, and the best protection for us both was silence. I had another partner for the admonition period. We told each other what we could and laughed when we had observed nothing, and enjoyed the moments that allowed us to speak to one another. We shared ideas of penance and encouraged one another. Every month the partners for the admonition period were changed. A notice appeared on the board in the Novitiate.

"The cattle are changing hands, and I have you," Sister Catherine said to me one afternoon.

"Good," I said, "we won't have to watch, we already know how the land lies."

She smiled and turned away, and I wondered if I had offended her.

Later in the day, when the admonition period bell rang, I wondered how I could begin to tell Sister Catherine what I thought. I was still puzzling it out when she appeared with a swish of beads and her quick gestures.

"Save your breath," she said, "I have been told the same thing every day for a month."

"What makes you like that?" I asked.

"It is impossible to say. I have always been the same.

I am morose and lonely and there is nothing that can alter that."

I knew nothing then of her condition or that she should have been treated medically. Psychiatry was a word that was never spoken in the Novitiate. The system called upon the self-control of each member, and the sick in mind were left to fight out their own impossible battle. To understand her moods of depression and sullen behaviour was something that the Novice Mistress was not able to do. She shouted her orders of "control" like a drunken sergeant-major and tried to make Sister Catherine conform.

I started to watch her during the day, partly because she was my subject for admonition, and partly because she was looking so white and ill. She had periods of morose gloominess and she would be completely silent during the recreation periods. The Novice Mistress used to try and force her to make conversation. It was beyond her power, but the Mistress misunderstood and thought she was sulking.

"You must speak, Sister," she said to her. "You must consider the others at the recreation, and you must try to make their evening enjoyable."

"It's an intellectual exercise," she said to me. "I can feel nothing, there's nothing about which I wish to speak. I dislike the others and they dislike me."

"It isn't true," I said. "They don't understand you, maybe, but there is no question of dislike."

"I don't dislike them, but I feel nothing for them."

"Perhaps you should leave?"

"What shall I do? Can you imagine what use a failed nun is in Ireland. They look on you as though you were some kind of a witch. My father would feel ashamed, and my mother would never look at the neighbours again. There is no question of my returning home."

83

"You are qualified," I said. "You could get a job in England, you could make friends outside." I realised when I had said this that I was speaking of the land outside the convent as though it were a foreign region we were fearful of treading. This was what the convent had been doing to us during the months we had been there, we had become strangers to our own people. We had undertaken a task at which our relatives could not bear to think we would fail. If we wanted to return to our own homes, our own countries, we would be as strange as though we had never seen them before. Sister Catherine was frightened and ill, and there seemed nothing I could do.

I tried to speak to the Novice Mistress.

"She must learn self-control, Sister."

It was the same answer whatever the complaint. I decided I must ask the advice of the priest who came to the confessional each Saturday.

We waited our turn outside the confessional. We knelt upright trying to think of something to confess. These Saturday confessionals in the convent must have been the most boring the priest had ever experienced. There was never anything, I am sure, that would have made the priest sit bolt upright. I saw him one day playing noughts and crosses. He must have been tired waiting for the next novice, and had started a game with an imaginary opponent.

"The Bishop, perhaps," I thought, "he gets his own back on an imaginary Bishop when he should be listening to my sins." I was sorry to interrupt the game on that occasion and felt that the crushing of the fat Bishop was more important than the priest. Then, as on this Saturday, he gave me his divided attention.

"Bless me Father for I have sinned." The same rigmarole each week.

"How long is it since your last confession?"

He must have known that the novices came at this time every Saturday, but this impersonal note was to help one to have the feeling of anonymity.

"A week," I said.

I would have liked to say five years to hear his exclamation, but I resisted the temptation. After all, we believed that the priest took the place of Christ. Christ in His little box again, I thought.

"I have spoken twice after the Great Silence and thought uncharitably about one of the other novices, and been careless about my prayers."

I hurried with my tale of sin. I was always slightly embarrassed, although I had done this every Saturday since I was six years old.

"Say three Hail Marys, my child." He fumbled over his Latin forgiveness that was nothing more than the words of polite dismissal.

"I have a question to ask you, Father." My hands were sweating and rubbing against one another as though they belonged to someone else. I crossed my ankles over one another beneath the black dress, and the crucifix on the penitent's side of the confessional looked down on me reproachfully.

"What is it?" he asked. His tone sounded conspiratorial and I mistook it for interest. Perhaps he thought he would hear something that would interest him.

"It is one of the novices," I said. "She's ill. I'm sure of it. There is no one to help her."

"What's wrong with her?"

"She looks so morose and lonely, and sometimes looks

ill." As I said it I knew I had failed to explain properly. Whatever the answer it would be inadequate because I had not explained the problem. I had not made it clear her parents would be ashamed to have her back, and that she had had the same illness since her adolescence. Whatever mistakes I made in the framing of the question I had never expected the answer to be so stereotyped.

"Does the Novice Mistress know?" he asked.

"Yes, yes."

"What does she think?"

"She says she must control herself, Father, but she does not have the strength, it is something that is beyond her control."

"Nothing is beyond our control, she must pray to your holy founder and all will be well. Now say three Hail Marys and pray for me."

The hands behind the small wire window were making the blessing and the figure of the cross was being drawn by the blind eyes over the confessional. He was unable to see, he would not understand. It was as though a blind beggar had drawn his white stick over the pavement with an incomprehensible message.

I left the confession. I prayed for him, he needed it.

Withal the season passed with the self-imposed penances of the monastic madness of the youthful observance. The silence, the fasting, the rigid observance, the admonitions and the general desire to be a perfect model of the rule held us all together through the season of impossible depression. Yet it was in this season that we made the most progress. There were no interruptions, nothing to interfere with the pursuit of virtue. We were concentrated solely on

86

our own perfection, and not on the outside sphere which became increasingly unreal as the weeks passed on.

We learnt the rule and recited it verbatim on our knees to the Mistress of Novices, who corrected our slightest deviation in the recital. The "discipline" was used again by the nervous and strong alike. Other penances were given by the Mistress for faults committed, or self-imposed according to the feeling one had for Christ who, liturgically, was suffering the forty days in the desert.

It was at this time I began to understand that in its fullness the rule demanded that one accept not only the blame for the faults one had committed, but also learn to take the blame for mistakes that were not one's fault. This being "a fool for Christ" was expressly stated in the rule and made this demand of those who sought perfection. This was the special season of remembrance of Christ at the pillar and in the white robe of the fool. In order to comfort Him I tried to make a speciality of this virtue.

My first opportunity came some weeks later when the Mistress called me into the square room of admonition and, telling me to kneel, with eyes cast down I was berated for my noisiness in the dormitory the previous evening. Knowing that at the time I had been in the cell, silent and praying, I felt certain that I was not the offender. But to offend in this way against the rule of silence was very serious and required that a penance be suffered and public sorrow be expressed. At once the protection of the old world rose to my rescue, but I pushed aside the help and joined in the spirit of the new life that demanded so many strange things. I made no sign of disagreement, and asked for permission to beg the pardon of the community who had been so outraged at my disrespect for the specially silent hour.

All during the day I waited anxiously for the evening

87

when the entire convent, choir nuns, novices and lay sisters, would be gathered in the refectory for the evening meal, and would stand in their rows with their heads bowed and their hands clasped waiting for me to speak my fault to the gathered groups.

They waited like sympathetic vultures, sorrowful that the carnage must take place, and yet they waited for the kill. Trembling I moved to the centre of the wide room where there was no friendly eye or kind hand. I knelt awkwardly on the floor, embarrassment making the movements difficult. The fear of kneeling was only surpassed by the fear that I might not be able to stand again graciously and bow politely to the unsinning group before me.

I begged their permission to tell my fault and ask their pardon which was given to me by the Superior on behalf of the community. I knelt in front of them all, alone as I had never been before alone. The words, rehearsed a hundred times during the day, would not find their way out of my mouth which was dry and trembling. I had to confess to take the blame as He had taken the blame. I did not want their forgiveness, I only wanted oblivion. Finally the traditional words of sorrow came out of the mouth that seemed new and strange to me. I was publicly forgiven by the Superior who admonished me and told me to say the traditional prayers. The grace followed immediately on confession and my moment of humiliation passed and joined the long line of traditional monastic penances. I had made one contribution to the record.

As the meal commenced I could feel the food choking me in the ever watchful atmosphere. The rawness of my nerves made me shudder and wait with an unusual distress for the end. Were they all watching me? I wondered, and felt their eyes bored through the raw flesh of shame that covered me.

When this had passed, and later when I lay in the dormitory covered in the blue bed, away from all the surrounding shame, I wondered about the truth of the rule that advised so difficult a thing. It was strange to recommend as virtue something that was not even true. I had suffered the humiliation and had taken the blame, and hoped that God-Christ was happy. I fell into sleep as I thought on this.

9

AS THE weeks of Lent progressed I watched the senior novices prepare for their profession. They were thrust at the beginning of the Lenten season into a three months' retreat in preparation for the consecration that was to take place. They were allowed even less freedom than the rest of us, and were banished into a land of total silence and abnegation. I watched them as they sewed the linen and the black cloth of the habit. Each stitch seemed to me to hem them further into their world of solitude. I watched them as they moved their lips and needles in a strangely mixed union.

They had seen nothing of their families during the three months of waiting. They were forced to make their selection between Christ and the world without parental help, without help of any kind. They were instructed in the meaning of the three vows that were to be taken. Poverty and obedience were discussed with the utmost theological accuracy, whilst chastity was passed over in euphemisms and polite refrain. They were incapable, I thought, of discussing this vow with the same accuracy. It was many years later that I realised the Mistress knew as little as I, maybe even less.

They were firm in their intention, the seniors of the group. Many had returned home during the two years in the Novitiate, these last three, however, were staunch supporters of Christ and had no intention of giving way. They were not tempted at this stage. They had no illusions that they would work better in the world. Like the children whom they would teach they were concerned with the present, and the temptations of the future were out of their reach.

The season, like all seasons, passed with surprising rapidity and we seemed to reach the end of Lent as quickly as we had been rushed into the beginning. We were in the Sunday of the Palm and the Hosanna'd song as I was beginning to fall into the routine and be happy in the new silence.

On the Sunday the children in the convent chapel bore the palms with the look of tiny woodcutters who had been surprised into an early morning cutting. They were no longer oppressed by the dark ashes, but were in happy singing lines driving the imaginary donkey with swishing tail through the chapel and the little garden that led to the entrance. The nuns joined the line of children who had found their God in the early morning rising. They were all singing; the Friday of Agony had not yet come. Christ was on the Donkey, riding around the grounds in state with the green palm swinging round his head. The breakfastless voices rose in the chapel, and the children shouted out the Hosannas with the same joy as the Judaic children of the past Sunday.

The Mass began, and the long gospel of the Passion was read. The glory had gone, and the fidgeting children began to feel the pain of the gospel of the Passion. It was long and tedious, and they rubbed their ankles against the pews as they tried to find some relief from the weary standing. They stood stork-like, with one white-socked leg in evidence against the brown bench.

The Sunday of the donkey passed and the real week of Lent drew in. I found the atmosphere oppressive. We were not at this time concerned with our own sufferings, we were lost completely, all of us, in the sufferings of Christ.

We sent the children back to spend their Passiontide with their parents. I had helped to pack them into buses that could not move sufficiently quickly for the impatient passengers who were racing out of the land of sorrow and purple statues to the warm homes of the Easter egg. I had been sad when the bus moved down the path of cracks and had covered their wishes with its round wheels, and had pushed into oblivion the remembered days of the teaching term.

For us the Spikenard was just beginning to be poured. We had the last week to bear in the total silence of the childless world, the passing of which had recalled forgotten fathers and mothers who no longer afforded the least protection. The severing which Christ had foretold took place for us on this day.

We went down in spirit into Bethany where He was suffering on the Monday and thought about Martha and Mary, and the economic Judas Iscariot who managed the money.

The week passed in a silence of pain and passion. The thrashing cord switched its way, like the donkey's tail, throughout the convent in the week of suffering. Thursday began the final twenty-four hours of agony.

The Mass for the Thursday began with the glorious hymns

of the Communion. Its beginning was joyful; we were re-calling in the bells and music the joy of the wonderful feast, the first great Feast of the Bread. After the Feast the bells and the music would be heard no more until the Easter bell would call on us all to rise again.

The convent would drop into the sad silence of the mourning season.

The traditional clappers of the mourning church would re-echo throughout the convent like the death rattle, and the sad chant of the season would float through the church without the accompaniment of the organ.

The Mass ended, and the community waited to pray by the altar of repose where the body of Christ was placed in the bread, and the main altar was left bare.

During this time the devotion in the community was maintained throughout the night. The Christ in the bread was never left alone. His sojourn in the garden was re-membered by the nuns during the night. We rose, two by two, in the cold dark hours of the early morning, and changed places with each other every half hour in the wrought pews in the side chapel.

We stayed with Him in spirit from the moment that Judas ran from the room with the silver clutched in his Jewish hands that had dipped into the dish of betrayal. He had run, this man of tiny values, out into the night that was the first move in the circle of the dawn that was to bring the crucifixion to the willing God, who was wash-ing the feet of His men in the room at the top of an un-known house. It was here that the boxing of Christ had begun; of His own free will He had allowed the outrage whilst He threatened His lost friend with damnation in the time to come. The protesting eleven carried out the form of the loyalty but ran even faster than Judas when the moment came. The crowing cock chased them into the oblivion of the unknown and the unknowing. They slammed the doors of memory in His face and left Him to sweat the blood like drizzling rain in the garden wet already with the fallen dew that awaited the dawn for its release. There was no release for Him or for Judas, or for the conforming eleven, they all had to suffer as the God of the clouds that allowed the dew to fall had ordained.

It had seemed to me so short a time since they had been calling on Him to come in the circled childhood, and now I remembered a conversation I had had earlier with the Novice Mistress.

"Was it us or God the Father who trapped Him?" I had asked. "Why when a twist of a finger of the Almighty could have saved the world did He reduce the body of Christ to this blood-sweating figure of huddled humanity?"

"It was the will of God, and it is not for us to question that." She turned over some letters on the desk and held them between her fingers like wasted prisoners.

It seemed to me that there was no escape, we were prevented from asking questions, and were pinned down into this existence of ours like the letters on the desk.

"We're trapped, all of us, Him and us," I said. "We pray for the world but it makes no difference. He had to go through it all, no matter what we do now, to expiate the sins of the world."

"You know what the Church teaches, Sister, I have nothing to add to that." The Novice Mistress looked at the door and then at me.

"Have you no duties to perform just now, Sister?"

"Yes," I said, and moved slowly from the room.

This ever-existing Abraham, I thought, would have His Son suffer that He might be appeased. The Son or His

94

people could writhe out their agonised hour of life, and He might, or might not, be pleased in the end.

But it was His total loneliness that touched me above all. He had been betrayed by His friends and ignored by His Father, and left under the swaying tree with all the surrounding misery of an orphaned child. He had looked for comfort and repeated His prayer of desperate hope, and had been ignored. We had been taught that He saw us here now, here in the early morning of the cold chapel, and for His sake I hoped this was so.

Whilst He lay there with His blood trickling over the ground already sodden with the fallen grapes, He saw Judas. The cord that had tied Him to Christ was twisted around his neck in umbilical union as he swung out of the terrible earth into a fearful heaven like a deranged trapeze artiste. The dangling of the soul in the cold wind of the reality of sin had shocked me, and indeed Christ, into the terrible wonderment of despair on behalf of Judas.

As he dangled before me, with his sin entangling him in the new world of complexity and punishment, I was awakened from my thinking by the bowing black nun who had come to release me and send me back to the dormitory, that I might forget the agony briefly for the remaining hours of the night.

I could not leave Him to battle on His own, and went back to the dormitory to continue to suffer with Him. I adopted a not unusual practice of novices, spending the remainder of the night on my knees in the tiny cell, burying my face in the blue coverlet and thinking of Him as they dragged Him now to the pillar and finally dressed Him in the ever present purple of the statues. I saw Him with the thorns pressing into His white forehead. I was sorry for Him then. The problems that worried me before passed in the union of the dark night of suffering.

The morning of the Friday came without the chance of Communion. We were denied even this, the final denial of the Lent. For those who had denied themselves food and drink during the six weeks of waiting this was the final moment of culmination. We went to the chapel that was in complete mourning and chanted the office that bewailed the agony of Christ, while at the same time praising the Great God in Greek and in Latin, as though the change in words would bring about the miracle of the saving of the Son. I had, when a child, thought that if I besought God enough He would not force Christ to suffer in this way. I had not realised then that it was past, and even now I found it difficult to recognise the non-existence of His present time suffering. During these days it was as though He really was in the ring again, battered against the ropes that tied Him into the fight.

We had to spend this day in the traditional silence and penance of the monastic communities the world over. Meal times, which were always difficult, became more so on this day than ever before. That He might be comforted we all, Superiors and Juniors alike, sat on the floor to eat the meal He had provided. How could this comfort Him who had been thrown out from the Kingdom to join the criminals who were erected like banners in the world of sin? They flapped in the wind, Christ and the thieves, as we squatted on the floor. We ate in darkened and mournful silence. Afterwards the clapper rang throughout the house and we went again to the chapel and reiterated the words of the Passion. We moved around the chapel in pretence of the calvaried walk, genuflecting at intervals when we recalled His falling by the roadside. We said the traditional prayers of comfort as we remembered His walk along the road to the terrible end.

Finally the third hour came and we were mournful.

The day then passed in silence and in worship of the Cross. We went, all of us, to kiss the cross the priest held in his hand as he stood safe on the altar, surrounded by the black nuns who venerated it, kissed it, and returned to their places making their reparation.

After the death at the third hour we sat in the embarrassed groups of the funeral mourners. We did not know what to do in this hour of outraged tragedy, and we waited at the funeral feast, lost and forlorn.

It passed like other funerals and deaths, the trivia of the day penetrated, and we worked at the cleaning and the polishing which in the penitential season had become our routined existence.

The hymn of mourning went through the convent.

> *O my people what have I done to thee?*
> *Wherein have I grieved thee?*
> *Answer me.*

We recalled in the psalm the bounty of God that they had rejected, and then, finally, the joy in suffering became evident. The tradition on which the Church was founded was reiterated throughout the greyness. Joy had come to humanity from the wood. In the crucifying of Christ joy had come to the world.

Then the Byzantine Christ filled the church. In the *Vexilla Regis* the mystic glory of the Cross shone out on to the world.

We moved then into the light of the Saturday and waited patiently for the final glory of the Sunday. The midnight vigil of the Saturday was one of joy and expectation. The

97

darkness of the chapel was soon to be lit with the brightness of the Pascal candle that would shine out and greet us in the midnight hour. This festival of light, this changing of the darkened hour, filled the house with happiness. We entered the chapel, in the silence of the mournful hour of eleven, like children expecting a reward for the labours suffered during the long Lent.

As the final clapper of the season sounded throughout the whole monastery we made our way in the recollected groups warm with the sanctity of the past weeks. I was reminded of the prophecies that we read at this time. The Lord looked down on the Egyptians and crushed them with His wheel, and saved Israel. "What can we do against Israel?" they had asked, "since the Lord is on their side?" I felt now, as in the glory of the Easter morning we all felt as we bent at the benches of prayer, that the Lord was on our side, there was no more fighting against the world that had sent out the song of luxury when we were weary. We were past all this now; we had survived the famine in the desolate land.

The harshness of the season began to pass as the Sacristan prepared for the light that was to come in the darkness. The sea of sadness recoiled as the hand of Christ was seen to rise in blessing over the waters that had pressed us since the day of the ashes. Since the moment of the memory of our sins had been evident on that morning we had had no respite. Now the happiness for which we had been born was coming again in the flame of love symbolised in the candle. The Light of the World was coming again, in His love, to save us from the anger of the Father who might have left us to our destruction had it not been for the Son who had felt we were worth salvation.

We prayed then, each one, in the ordered manner of the

98

Liturgy, rising at the "Levate" and falling at the "Flecta-mus genua" as we were told on the printed page of the unused book of Easter prayer. Finally, as we prepared for the beginning of the Easter Mass, the great light began to be seen. The darkness of the chapel lifted gradually as we took from each other the light from the Festive candle. The first nun lit the candle and passed the altared light around like the charitable word.

Soon we were all standing with the candles of the wonderful night in our hands, and the chapel glowed as never before. The light of Easter was new to me. I had never before seen such innocence and light joined together in so bright a union. We had ceased to mourn; the darkness had gone; the voice of the risen Christ rang out through the church—"I am with you!"

He had come back, the bloodiness of his murder was gone. In the joy of the Easter song we could be happy once again. We were happy at His new found safety, His triumph over death. "Greet this day with rejoicing, let us be happy together!" the Liturgy cried. We knelt with comfort, and out of custom, pressed our knees in penance against the bench. We had forgotten, momentarily, that the season of penance was past.

The Mass progressed and we received Him in the Communion of Rising. Then the night ended with the warmness of Easter. We left the chapel and took the warm drink given in honour of the feast, and silently went to bed to reflect on the wonderful mystery that had taken place.

The next day we spoke at the happy breakfast that celebrated His rising. The bell rang in the bleak refectory and we rejoiced totally and completely for the first time since I had come. The rising of Christ was the most important feast in the Church, and we were all happy.

I longed to go to the garden where the Easter sun was shining, where the birds were coming back and the sea was lolling in the backward flow I loved.

The breakfast ended with the small bell's tinkle, and I was free. Free to feel the sun and enjoy the cry of the birds in the loved wind that was blowing with the new breeze of Christ throughout the land. I had come through the liturgical cycle. I had won the first round of the battle in the ring that held so many unfair opponents whose blows sometimes surprised me. I watched the senior novices who glowed with the triumph of their survival, and prepared with longing for the moment of dedication.

They would leave the Novitiate and enter the convent proper. They who were my friends would no longer talk to me, and would avert their eyes when we met, according to the rule. They had made their choice and would take their vows and go. I, and the others who were my companions, would then be the senior members, and we would take their responsibilities and trials.

The day of profession came, and the groups went silent and unknown, as they had come, to work for ever in the convent of diverse penance.

10

WHEN THE senior novices left to become full members of the order there were many changes for us who were left. I was now in a period of semi-authority and no longer felt so alone. There were new postulants to be cared for and instructed.

The weather was changing and the first signs of summer began to show themselves. There was a new glint on the sea and the gulls rested on the garden paths more frequently. Even their cry seemed less harsh.

With the new season there were new regulations for us. We were now allowed to walk along the shore and the cliffs. The rocks on the beach looked as though someone had been scrubbing them during the winter. We used the smaller ones as stools and sat looking at the sea. It seemed calmer now than I had ever remembered it. The storm had passed over the waters and it lapped its way cheerfully as we stood there. Children came to the beach with their parents. Families full of noise and calls competed with the birds and contrasted with our quiet groups. We watched them as they swam and felt pity and envy as the small children were knocked over by the waves.

They called to each other, and I listened to their talk

with a certain nostalgia. Children have this effect on everyone from time to time. They are so absorbed in what they do. Their whole lives that summer seemed to revolve around the swaying sandcastle and the ridges drawn in the sand. Walking along the shore one could see the small rivulets the incoming tide had made on the lines they had drawn.

"It's gone!" we heard them cry when they came to look for their swaying architecture. They mourned over their lost castles as we mourned for our lost homes, but they were allowed to express their grief.

"It's been ruined by the sea and my sixpence has gone." The hiding of small coins in this precarious bank was a common hobby and no loss seemed to dissuade them.

We wanted to swim. It was watching the children that made the restriction so hard. We finally plucked up the necessary courage. Sister Catherine was the least timid and made our request for us.

"The Irish sisters swim," she told the Novice Mistress.

"It's different here," was the reply.

"We could manage to do it without causing a stir."

"Stir or no stir there is no chance of this permission being granted."

Even so we were relaxed with the holiday, the easy rule, the later rising, the different food, the long walks. All of these things had stopped the terrible depression that had been overcoming me. We had begun to live again and to breathe more easily. The room no longer oppressed me and the rule was no longer so cruel. I had become acclimatised to the new world that demanded so much and yet at times seemed to demand so little. We had food and clothing and warmth and sleep. We had, in fact, everything except something that was our own.

I was twenty-one during that summer, and felt fearful that I should have reached that period of my life with so little knowledge of the world and the problems it contained. I was confined completely with my own troubles, and it was at times like this I thought of the world as a whole. I seemed to be cut off and concerned entirely with my own thoughts and aspirations. Perhaps it was the life rounded and curtailed into a self-centred existence that made me so oblivious to everything else around me.

The gifts and presents from my home awakened my interest momentarily. The Novice Mistress was amazed at the sort of gifts that came.

"I thought your people would have known by now what was suitable for a religious and what was not," she remarked as she went through each parcel.

"There is some soap here that is not suitable for your use." She left it on one side for the poor. I could feel the scent through the wrapping and envied the poor. The last parcel was small and compactly wrapped as though containing some treasure. I watched the unfolding of the string like a guest of honour at an unveiling ceremony.

"It's a pen," she said.

I looked at the gift my parents had sent. A small black pen with a circle of gold. The only pen I possessed was an ancient model which I had collected from some unwanted lost property.

"Do you have a pen, Sister?" she asked.

"Yes." I was thinking of the brown leaking monstrosity. "It isn't very good though." I faltered a little as I said this, yet she did not seem to notice.

"Well, that's fine, Sister, there will certainly be some novice who has need of one."

"But it's mine." I protested weakly this time.

"Indeed it is, and a good chance for self-sacrifice. You may continue to own the one already in your possession, but a good religious never has two of anything."

She packed it away neatly as though interring my parents in the neat folds of the paper. I left the room with the trivia that the presents had yielded, and a pain caused by the denial of my rights.

The next day I saw another novice using the pen. I ached to touch it again. I wanted, as it were, to hold a piece of my home between my fingers and look at it. My parents had touched the pen. This became my obsession. To the other novice it was simply a pen; for me it became a symbol of my home and I needed it. I felt if I could hold it once more some of the warmth of the home I had lost would return. I had not seen my parents for a year. I often wondered what it was that prevented their coming. Was it the crossing of the sea they found so difficult, or the embarrassment of finding their daughter in a fancy dress they could not understand? Whatever the reason they did not come.

It was not the pen I wanted but just to touch their gift, to feel the present their hands had held and wrapped. The idea began to possess me, to have the pen in my hand and to press close between my fingers the touch that had gone forever.

For days on end I waited like a cautious thief for opportunity to touch the pen.

One day when I was delayed on my way to the chapel and all the others had gone I entered the Novitiate for a book I had forgotten. I saw the pen coffined like a swaddled baby in its white box.

I clutched the pen firmly between my fingers and waited for the surging feeling of warmth I had thought would permeate me. There was nothing, and once again I felt betrayed by the reality of things. Life it seemed was as it was, signs and symbols meant nothing. They were gone out of my life, and all my feeling for them had disappeared without warning. They had fallen into the abyss of my past life which for me no longer existed and which I could no longer reach. I was fearful then lest my family should ever come, for if they did, I thought, they would be as unreal to me then as they were now.

I left the room and made my way to the chapel where the evening song of the church was being sung. The sad chant of the hymn went up to the heavens and I knelt in the pew, numbed and puzzled.

Later, when I went out to the garden, I realised that the summer was passing. The year of final training was beginning for me, and the numbness was a good thing. It would see me through the second autumn that would demand more than the fallen leaves from the garden. I knew that I would suffer in these months to come. The separation would be final. I would make my way to the land of reality, and suffer at my loss, but the end would be glorious. I would be crowned as the bride of Christ in the ceremony of the profession that had begun to mean so much to me.

I worked so that the miracle of the change could take place. The new cycle of life was beginning, and yet I did not mind. I felt pain for the newcomers who came with the surprised look of the beginner. I remembered my own agony of the ever-present bread, and was careful at all times to help them. I heard them crying for the homes that had gone, as though there had been a war and they had, all of them in the white convent, been orphaned by the blitz.

The storm that had come squalling into the new world was a bitter experience, and the gulls, as they flew over my head, seemed to understand and swoop down with a look of comfort they could not sustain. They were so impatient for the heavens and, as I approached them, they went. They were not shy of me like my family, but they were afraid of captivity, and they circled sadly as I moved, reluctant to leave me, but too cautious and wild to stay.

But the reality of the passing was finally borne in on me and the others who were my equal. We prepared, as the year progressed, for the profession. We would, in this year, beg permission of the community to join them, and we would be accepted if the Council considered us fit.

I soon knew that the criterion of this Council was outward observance, they had no other choice but to choose those who could maintain the silence and walk in the customary way. All eccentricity was dismissed at once as an evil. We must all be the same to survive. The rule of the sixteenth century was to be observed in full.

I began to be strained, and as the three months of silence began I was afraid. We were so isolated, all of us, as we worked in a world that was cold and unfriendly. We needed each other and yet would never admit the need. I had needed company, but here in the Novitiate all friendship was considered harmful. I had come into a sphere that considered no one but Christ, and we were, never at any time, unless we were ill, considered in any way at all. Those who could not sustain this total abnegation were ill, again and again. I could not allow myself this luxury. The strength that had carried me through the desert upheld me now, as the loneliness dragged on.

Before the silence of the three months' retreat my mother had come to the sea-surrounded convent. Yet to me it was as though she had never been. She spoke of people whom I knew and could not really remember. The new curtains and the new car passed into my world, and out again, like the breath of wind in the garden. They were not important or relevant to the months of silence of which we were just beginning to think.

II

THE SILENCE of the three months began with
special prayers and penances, and once it had begun
I could remember no other life. I was happy; there
were no distractions. I concentrated solely on the perfection
of the outward observance and the wonderful peace the
silence brought me. The peace was unexpected. I had expected to suffer, yet these three months were the happiest
I had ever known, or would ever know in this life. Like
the other novices whom I had observed from afar the previous year I made the habit. We sewed the black cloth
in the silence of the retreat room, and made the garment
that would fold us for ever into the arms of Christ.

When we entered into the period of the three months'
silence it was no longer possible for me to keep in touch
with Sister Catherine. We were together often but we were
allowed no conversation. Nothing had been done to alleviate her trouble and I watched her day after day becoming more white and strained. She looked very ill and yet
there was nothing I could do. I could not approach the
Mistress of Novices nor the priest, I had tried that already.

There was no opportunity to speak so it was difficult
to say how morose this novice had become. Her expression

was one of sullen ill humour which by this time I recognised as part of her illness. Her behaviour was strange and different. She sat by herself in the farthest corner of the room, staring out of her black eyes which seemed to have taken on a look of hopeless resignation. The dark circles were now black, and the dreary weather left her looking cold and forlorn. She was pathetic and I wanted more than anything else to speak to her, but the rule at this time was extremely strict and there was no opportunity. I watched her as often as I dared whilst we sewed in the Novitiate and noticed her progress was slow. One afternoon when we were together by ourselves I was tempted to speak. In order to overcome the temptation I concentrated on the work I was doing. A sniff, more informative than those I remembered during the recreation period, startled me, and I dared to look up. There were tears running down her face. The unthreaded needle was making a pretence of sewing and she looked wild and distracted. I could bear it no longer and went over to her.

"What is it?" I asked, startled at the tremor in my own voice.

"Nothing," was the only word I could get from her.

"Are you ill?" I said. There was no need for the question, the answer was obvious.

"You mustn't speak, and there's nothing for you to do in any case."

At that moment I hated the whole organisation, the while inhuman existence that these three peaceful months had now become. There were times when they forced you to speak, and others when it seemed so necessary to talk it was forbidden. I hated the whole life at that moment as on the morning when I threw the bread.

I went straight away to the Mistress of Novices. It was

my anger that made me so brave and I needed to get there before it had cooled.

I knocked sharply on the door and the Novice Mistress turned and looked surprised to see me at such an unusual time.

"What is it, Sister?" she asked, as she continued to read the papers on her desk. "Has war been declared that you come rushing in like this?"

"It's Sister Catherine, Mother, she is ill, really ill, I'm certain of it."

"Have you been speaking in the Novitiate?"

"Yes," I said, "surely it can't be such an enormous offence when the need is so great."

"If her need is so great I am here, Sister. There is someone for her to speak to if she feels it necessary. You have no permission to speak or to take on my duties in my absence."

"I wasn't taking on your duties, Mother. It was only charity to speak to her, she's dreadfully distressed."

"Well, now you are assured that there is a proper course for her to take there is no need for you to continue to break the rule. Get on with your duties, Sister, and I will continue with mine."

I kissed the floor in the usual way and, weighed down by the futility of trying, moved towards the door.

Later that day I saw the Novice Mistress speak to Sister Catherine. Later I noticed her place in chapel was empty. I was glad to think of her resting. She did not appear the next morning at Mass and I was glad that she was having the rest she needed so badly. She did not appear any day that week and I had become accustomed to her empty place and had nearly forgotten the whole incident.

One day later in the week I passed the Novitiate infirmary and thought I would smile my good wishes to her, and even though we could not speak I thought this might let her know that I had not forgotten her. I put my hand on the door where I knew she would be sleeping. The room was empty and there was no sign that anyone had been there at all. I knew then that she had gone. Home perhaps, but certainly gone, and I had not even said goodbye. My keeping of the rule of strict silence had caused us to part without so much as one word or a sign. I never heard from her again.

After Sister Catherine had gone I felt lonely for a time, but as the days passed I gradually forgot that she had been there in the Novitiate. I became engrossed once again by the small details of the rule, the tiny circumspections began to concern me more and more.

I had even forgotten Sister Angela who had not been in the Novitiate at all for many weeks, or maybe it was only some days. I hadn't thought of her. Her continual ill health made her absence in the chapel and around the Novitiate room quite unremarkable.

We were at evening meditation when a notice was passed around the chapel that we were to go at once to the Mistress of Novices. When I arrived there I found the other novices already gathered. The Mistress motioned us into the Novitiate and we flocked in there awaiting the announcement, thinking that some fault was about to be corrected in public. The Novice Mistress looked distressed and quiet.

"Sisters, I have called you here to tell you that Sister Angela is ill, very ill, I ask your prayers. You may go up now and quietly sit in her room. The prayers for the dying will be recited, so bring your manuals with you."

We started to speak all at once but she left the room. As she had overlooked completely our flagrant breaking of the silence room I knew the position was very serious. We took our manuals from the drawer and quickly made our way to the small room. Afterwards I wished I had not gone there and I am sure there were many who felt the same.

Sister Angela was lying with her eyes closed and her hands lying listlessly on the cover. I had heard often the description of dying people who pluck at the covers and had thought it an old wives' tale. I watched her now, weak and in agony, the white hands hopelessly plucking a little life from the covers, whilst her laboured breathing could be heard in the small room. It was as if she were creating life rather than just on the point of dismissing it from her grasp for ever. The book from which the vows were read was on a small table. She had made her death-bed vows, the privilege of novices who had seriously intended to take the vows when their time was ready. Poverty, chastity and obedience. She lay there possessing nothing, even life itself was to be taken from her, she lay in the arms of death, obedient because all her resistance had gone. Everything around her was a chaste white—the sheet, her clothing, even her face. She was dying as she had lived. I had known sinners and the tepid depart life more comfortably and it seemed cruelly unfair.

Out of the depths I have cried to Thee, O Lord;
Lord hear my prayer.

The voices were saying the age-old prayer and the sound circled around the wilting candles. The orange candles that surrounded the death bed were like trembling searchlights, and the smoke, like the departing soul, disappeared and passed without a sound.

The voices were still chanting.

And let my cry come unto Thee.
If Thou O Lord will mark iniquities,
Lord who shall endure it?

There was moisture on her lips as we prayed and I hoped the Novice Mistress would wipe it away. I watched it all the time. I could not pray because I wanted to remove the small white drops. They lingered on her chin as though they were alive and were unwilling to leave her. Life was slowly leaving her and I could not pray at all. The voices chanted on and I felt fainter with every syllable. The darkness of the room and the orange glow haunted me. I wanted her to die. The voices praying for her life were a mockery. She had had her life of pain. Why couldn't they let her go? "For God's sake die," I thought to myself. "Die and leave them here to carry on with life they find so sweet. Let them labour on, but surely this breathing will be your last labour."

There had been many stories of the labourer who had gone home happily when the work was done. "Why keep her here? There is nothing for her to have now. She has experienced it all, the pain, the parting from her home, the work and the routine, all of it she has suffered. Why do we ask her to take it up again?"

For with Thee there is merciful forgiveness
And by reason of Thy word I have waited for Thee
                                                    O Lord.

From the morning watch even unto night
Let Israel hope in the Lord.

What was it they were hoping for now? "Let her die. Christ of the swaying hill lift her from their power and from their entreaties. Father forgive them, they know not what they do." I was praying this prayer as their orange chant went up with the coiling smoke. Their prayer might reach God before mine.

"God let her die now, let her die."

I had not intended to speak aloud but the voice came out in the gloom. I was chanting my own prayer aloud. I had let them hear my wish. Some hadn't noticed, they were intent on their prayer. The Novice Mistress glanced in my direction.

"Sit up, Sister, and keep in time with the others."

Keep in time. There was no time left. The orange candles were burning so quickly. At the sound of my unorthodox words Sister Angela opened her eyes and plucked gently at the cover on the bed. Even that small movement became fainter. She was sighing, and the breath came from her like the wind in the trees, moving in and out between the words of the chant it went up to heaven like incense. Now the voices were saying

I will go into the valley and the shadow of death
And fear no evil because Thou O Lord art with me.

Death's shadow was playing on the wall and then it terrified me. She had to go into this darkness without help, without the help of even the orange candles. Her whiteness would make her stand out in the darkness and the shadows would follow her. She feared the evil, I saw it in her eyes. She was tired of the world and terrified of death, but there was no choice for her. The path lay there wide and stark and she was afraid and there was nothing we could do. The prayers and the chanting, the smoke of the orange incense might rise but she faced the journey alone. She had the Viaticum, the bread for the journey, the Communion of protection, but she was afraid.

She died then with a long breath and a vague movement of her hands. She went out of a world she hardly knew and had only seen through the mirage of pain for which there had been no healing. And we knelt there and watched her.

In three days we had the funeral. The cold journey that was really already completed was re-enacted in our life. We stood first in the chapel and watched the parents who wept silently in the front. They were black robots, kneeling and rising without any feeling or understanding. Eventually the black mourning ceremony was over and we walked into the grounds carrying candles which shed no light on the black journey she had undertaken. We began to chant the *In paradisum* as we formed our line of honour. The melancholy chant rose and fell in the garden. *In Paradisum deducant te Angeli*—"May the angels guide you into paradise." The candles wavered in the wind or simply died, but we sent the soul out of the garden with the eerie chant. The sound of the hymn became indistinguishable with the birds' movements and the falling leaves. The parents of the body and soul that we chanted out of the earth followed in tiny funeral procession. Their heads were bent in bewilderment and they stumbled after the soul that flew under the angelic escort. They looked small and grey in the garden, powerless and numb. The tears they shed were small symbols and fell on their faces like leaves that mourn the passing summer. The life that they had made escaped before them into the gloom and they were not able to follow it. Their life and their reason for being was carried out in the shallow box. The end would begin when the box was lowered into the cold soil, and the loneliest sound in the world reverberated in the graveyard.

115

The thin mourning bell cried in the silence and the commencement of the new life was announced in the convent.

The term moved on and finally we were again in the Lenten season of penance and awaited the season of rejoicing. I awaited the coming of Easter with the joy and expectation of the season that had never touched me with much magnificence before. I felt unique and free, and, for the first time since my coming, a person of importance now that the time of my own profession drew near.

I had been chosen from out of the millions in the world. The words of the Liturgy came again and again to me. "I have chosen you. You have not chosen Me." So I was to go from the Novitiate like one of the first chosen people, only this time there was to be no confusion.

Now there seemed to be no desert to be traversed, but a land of hope awaited me. For the first time in a life that happiness had skirted with a brief gesture I was joyful.

Now that the garment was sewn and the parents informed, I awaited the hour of profession with impatience. I wanted the acknowledgement of my triumph. I had survived the tyranny of the unused land and was victorious. I walked like the Roman leader pushing the pilate weaklings into oblivion. I could do everything in the arms of God who sustained me in the new world of new demands. He died for me, I thought, and I lived for Him. The world swayed with the wonder of God, the garden blossomed with the joy of the coming Spring, and I felt the new strength this season always brings.

Now I did not want to leave the Novitiate. I knew that the moment of profession would mean immediate removal from the Novitate and the move to another convent where there would be unknown faces and new ideas and stricter superiors with perhaps even less understanding. Yet I could face now what would have been an impossibility a year previously.

I would go and leave the gulls who would still come and look for me in the garden and flap their wings with the impatient gestures of the untrammelled. Would they miss me as I them? I doubted this and thought of them with longing. According to the monastic custom we did not know where we would go until it was the day of our departure. I was longing to know, but there had been no mention of the matter, and I had not asked.

The day of profession had come. There was little difference in the convent that accepted dedication as the world irrelevance. We did not rise with the usual bell at six o'clock but were allowed, for our day of celebration, another half hour. As the bell resounded I lay and thought of the ordeal awaiting us. There was no greater hour on the earth I was sure. How many worldly brides lay as we now lay? They awaited the hour of their dedication to a man who would die and pass and leave them only with a memory of passing pleasure. For us, when the final hour would come, we would all be gathered together in the Land of Judgement.

As I lay in the bed I could not be sure if I would have chosen Him had it not been for the fear I felt. I wanted to serve Him willingly, but there had been many times when I had hoped He would allow me to pass into oblivion. I would always have been aware I had forsaken Him had I not gone on.

When I rose that morning I placed the new clothes around me and walked slowly to the chapel that was to witness my final sacrifice. There was nothing that could call me back. I went to the chapel with a feeling of new-ness, of purity, of holiness and isolation.

Already my family had come. Finally they had crossed the sea and come into the land the values of which were to them incomprehensible. They had wanted to bring me back, to stop me making the special dedication. Yet they knew they could not, neither the wild brothers who challenged the world with the strength of the new manhood that had come to them in the work of the new life, nor the father who had learnt much through pain and failure, and who now clenched the bench with the weariness of a man who, despite all his wisdom, had been defeated in the end. He had wanted there and then to stop me as I lay on the ground bent in dedication. I knew nothing, he thought, the world of motherhood had escaped me, and he was sad.

We four novices knelt before the Bishop. We knelt as we had knelt in the practice, without any movement. We were trained, and the estranged families were recognising for the first time the change in the children who had left their home two years previously.

The *Ecce Sacerdos Magnus* was sung by the choir, and our life seemed to pass out of the chapel to the God who sat on His throne waiting for the sacrifice.

We promised our dedication of Chastity, Obedience and Poverty in the rich world of wonder and sacrifice. The Mass and the Communion followed. The blasphemy that had threatened my entrance did not worry me now and, like the others, I accepted the Bread with thankfulness.

After the Mass and the *Te Deum* we went out of the chapel to celebrate the feast. We hurried to the room which held my father and mother and the whole family to whom I belonged, and of which once again I felt a part.

Unused to the black, my father had treated me with the customary politeness he showed to the nuns. When he recognised me the tears that had stayed in their well for two years moved to the surface, and the words of apology came with the new found waters. I had left him completely and he could not speak or understand. The new black clothes forced him into polite distance that as a father of a child he could not comprehend. He had wanted to hug me and instead he had bowed to the new image and cried. He had stood there amazed and sorry and could do nothing. As I touched his hand I could feel the two years of separation passing into oblivion. I remembered him and the wonderful conversations of the old time. Violently I wanted again those nights cut short by the stories that had never been finished through the sleepiness of the early hours. The nature that had then sought sleep was now awakened into a new sense of appreciation, now that there was no such moment. We were polite to each other and joined the groups that stood making up the celebrants of the breakfast of the brides whose groom had long since gone out of the world.

They rejoiced at the victory, those who had understood it the least. They celebrated as they were expected, and went home after the day of triumph. My father had trembled at the dedication, and my overt happiness had not comforted him. He had wanted for us his own joys and passed over all else as useless and unrecognisable.

12

I ADJUSTED TO the change brought about by the profession in everyday life. I was moved from the Novitiate immediately as though I were an infectious disease. They wanted me no longer, and the new convent had as yet not been informed of my coming. I was once again, like the gulls, homeless and wandering. The footloose life did not last long, however, and I made my way from the convent by the sea to one placed in the heart of the city in another country. I left the hills that had been a glorious wild home, and came with the swift movements of the train to the new city convent that promised much.

I knew some of the young nuns there and was welcomed by them when I arrived. They guided me in the first days in the life that was so different from the Novitiate. They were busy, all of them, not with the details I had been taught to observe, but with the business of life for which they had been trained. They fought with Education Committees and unreasonable Superiors. They worked in the universities and bore the misunderstandings with immense stoicism.

Just as I had grown accustomed to this new phase the order came for the changeover. I was to be moved immediately to a small convent. I had to go again to accept a new welcome in a new convent whose Superior I was to find difficult and unsympathetic.

When I arrived at the convent it was the smallness I noticed above all else. It was like a family house that had overgrown its eagerness to accommodate them all, but there was no family atmosphere, and I was homesick in the Community. I remembered the gulls and the space of the green hills, and the wonder of the water as it fought against the sand that was always there like a faithful friend and returned even when the fierce sea had covered it.

In this new convent they lived in a proximity I had never before known and I felt suffocated by the number of women in the squared house. The garden seemed always to be without flower and had so little to offer. The small paths curved tinily and sent me to re-walk their length like Japanese torturers when I moved in the shadowless garden.

I felt exposed all the time, there were eyes everywhere, and the self-conscious awareness that had threatened to overcome me previously came again.

Like the garden the house was square, small, and wanting in character, the Superior limited, unco-operative and insensitive. The total atmosphere was confined and repressive, and I felt hemmed into the new life with the thread of sharp restriction.

I studied during the day under the eyes that came from the shallow face. The sharp words came with a newness to me. I had forgotten that power could be misused and that subjects were vulnerable. I listened to the tongue that seemed so different from the image I had had of Superiors. I had always realised there must be power misused everywhere, but had never really expected to meet it.

I studied Latin for seven hours a day without respite and attended to my religious duties for the remaining hours.

The recreation allowed did not relax me. I felt the hard tongue that reproached and corrected as though this hour was the special hour of the Superior who had let everything fade except her own authority.

The summer passed without any change in the routine. I learnt to recognise the Community by their walk, their cough, their breathing, and at times the noise of their sleeping when the night did not close my eyes.

I worked for the examination that would bring me release and carry me out of this narrow school and lead me into the life of the university that would broaden my mind which was becoming cramped in the squared existence.

And it came, the examination that was to act like a key for me, unlocking the prison that had suddenly appeared, and in which I had found myself, I who had been the subject to neither crime nor punishment. I lived the hours of the examination which, for once, wanted my opinion. I expressed ideas that had lain latent during the repressive months. I wrote the answers to the questions as though I were speaking to an examiner who listened to my every word. I was grateful for his attention and did my best to please.

On the day the examination was completed I went to the refectory and noticed again a habit of the Superior that caused me extreme discomfort. She sat like a reigning queen above the Community, demanding their submission and respect. She drank her tea noisily. I always noticed this. She twisted her spoon around the saucer as though it were some vice that needed suffering to exterminate it. The silver spoon twisted in agony before me. I was sympathetic to it since it was treated like the young nuns who had come under the Superior's control. She moved them around in an agony that was all the more unbearable because of its potential permanence. I knew I would escape eventually. I felt a compassion for those who would be left, but knew I would take life in both hands when it was offered.

The results of the examination came when I least expected them, and this meant another change.

I was reunited in the late summer in the city convent with those who had been my friends. I dreaded ever having to return to this small convent that would have wrapped around me its horrid muffler in the mid-heat of the day. I was warm and happy in the city convent that overflowed with young life and hopeful ideals.

13

THE LAND which seemed like a fairy tale opened for me with the coming of autumn and the falling leaves. I went with the other nuns to the University which had stood for many years with its greying look on the unwise world of young people that presented itself each term. We joined the groups of young people from all over the world. I felt free as never before. Even the freedom of the gulls seemed now like a captivity to me. The mind and the brain were released and fulfilment was a possibility. The old cramped life of the little convent seemed very far away and I learnt rapidly and eagerly. The books were my friends who accepted me as the students could not. I was to them simply a reader and not an oddity.

The students in my class had looked at first with wonder at this black veiled brain that had come from nowhere and returned to the convent when the darkness of the night came down. They were amazed when I smiled and tolerant when I joked. They were not unwilling to speak to me but they found it difficult. I for my part liked them. They had no need of me yet they did not reject me totally. I watched them as they made their way in happy groups across the yard that was to them the paving stones of their new life.

I worked in the first term and wandered around the new world with the look of one as yet not initiated. I had wanted company at first, and later this need had gone completely. I was willing to smile and to appear as a symbol, as a believer in ideals that they took me for.

The Communists were close on the line of friendship, and they understood me better than the Christians who made demands on me and insisted that I be perfect while they enjoyed themselves.

I had often wanted to speak to the groups of students yet feared that I would not be welcome. I was greeted with politeness everywhere. The world was one of diplomacy. They said certain things when I came and refrained from others. They were never sure of me, and I was never sure when I scandalised them and when I did not.

There were days when I was not concerned about this. I worked on the medieval scholars and enjoyed the study of St. Anselem. The voice of the past that came through the history lectures enthralled me and brought about for me a new world of ideas and thoughts. The lecturers in this department were a wonder to me. I enjoyed their controversy and took sides as they gave their views. They treated me with respect always and yet never as a friend. I was, even in this world for which I had longed and for which I had studied, an outsider. I walked this saucer-edged life and pretended I did not notice. Yet I noticed every rejection, every moment and movement that put me out of their midst.

I had realised finally what the life in the convent had done to me and for me. They had, with their discipline and their training of silence and control, put me outside of the ordinary run of humanity. I did not yet know whether I was pleased or not.

14

A S THE term wore on I began to have a clearer vision of life, and to feel for the first time new sensations. The world was becoming important to me. Not for its material values but I was beginning to experience an affinity with people that had been denied me in the Novitiate. I was becoming aware of every pain suffered by mankind. The world took on for me the image of the struggling Christus. Every pain, every abuse, every obscenity took on a sacrilegious meaning. Every blow that was given, and every pain felt seemed to me firstly to pass through me and then on to the world.

It was in this year that I understood fully the pain of war and revolution. We had heard of it often before. The story told by our fathers was so much fairy tale, but during this period of my life the Hungarian Revolution took place.

The news of Hungary was thrown upon us suddenly. We were happy in our idleness and ignorance, and then, when we were least prepared, the political significance of the events there was suddenly important to us.

The morning had begun like all other mornings. The rising bell seemed to ascend from the depths of hell to call us and we went to the chapel thinking only of our own weariness. Enclosed and surrounded in the convent by our own tiny values we were, on that morning, oblivious to the needs of the world, concerned with our keeping of the rule, crossing our hands in the accustomed way and casting our eyes to the ground we had missed the trouble on the hill.

It was not until the lunch break at the University that I noticed the placards and the marching. Hungarians who huddled together on this 24th day of October were being forced into a realisation of death and disaster. They were standing close together seeking comfort from one another.

"It might not have reached our town," one said.

"They are ripping our people to pieces and you talk of your town," his companion replied. "It's our nation that's being destroyed, it's our dead that line the streets. What does it matter what town it is?"

"To me it matters whether it's my sisters who are murdered and raped. I feel for the others, but what I feel for them . . ." He broke off into Hungarian and I couldn't follow what he said. He needn't have said anything. The sweat on his forehead and the movement of his hands were enough.

I asked one man if he wanted to talk. His name was George and I did not know him well. The least I could do was to listen and I tried to offer this consolation.

"If only I knew that they were safe," he said. "My mother and my small sister, if only they have escaped in time. If there is a God, Sister, I think he must be sleeping. He has closed his eyes to us."

I thought of Nazi Germany, and there was nothing I could say. God had curled up once again, hedgehog like in his slumbers, and left them to wade out of their blood alone.

George went on talking as though I were not there and I was unable to follow everything he said. He lapsed into a Hungarian lament from time to time. Part of what he said I can recall.

"Men like myself throwing hand grenades, throwing them wildly and with no experience. Throwing them without knowing where they will fall. Murdering their own people in the fight they don't understand."

There was nothing I could say except that I would pray for the safety of his family, but words could not remove the glaze from his eyes and the fear from his heart.

There were demonstrations all the time, and it was as though the Hungarian scene was being enacted before our eyes. Hungarians drunk at early morning to numb their feelings stood on the tables speaking impassionedly about peace. It was words and words only, and they knew it, and for me God was hiding His head again.

George and his friend Laslo spoke at the student meeting.

"The Hungarians," Laslo said, "may be confused in their hatred of Rakosi and Gero who have kept them in bondage, but they are clear at least in their conception of Western idealism. They have learnt about the freedom that you take for granted. They are trusting you now and feel that you won't forsake them. They have gambled their lives on this surety and England can't forsake them now."

They clapped and cheered him, and the noise of the rising emotions could be heard in the hall, but above everything else one could hear the plodding of the procrastinating English feet. They would forsake them, they were unwilling to carry one more burden and they left it on one side with words of hot, sympathetic understanding. No matter what Hungarian student spoke, and despite our clapping, England would go on encouraging with words only.

When I returned to the convent the verbal display had begun there also. Like a firework performance on the days of celebration the words and prayers were sent up to the sleeping Godhead, and were thrown back in the faces of the petitioners as the murderous massacre took place.

As the groups in the University clustered around the wireless set that brought the news like a greying newsmonger the information about the revolution began as a slow rumour, and then took on a terrifying intensity. The news which bombarded the quiet of the convent seemed all the more macabre and horrible since we were forced to sit there and do nothing.

In the University some of the students felt the tragedy and said nothing. Others verbalised their worst fears. At first it seemed as though "Nagy will be the Saviour in this most confused battle that surrounds Buda and Pest." Later one was to hear, "Nagy hasn't the strength to guide an ice-cream cart." As the trouble progressed the image of Nagy as the Saviour was completed, he was taken before the pilates of the regime and remained silent.

The desperate messages that came from the wireless were harrowing, the cries for help were countered with words of encouragement from England and America, but Hungary continued to fight out her battle alone. It seemed to me that the evil forces had once more been let loose on the world and there was no way of preventing the tragic ending. We were safe and secure in the convent, the agony of the Hungarian women seemed so far away, parcelled in the same box as the problems of China and its overpopulation, and the irrevocable harm that had been done to the Jewish people. The nuns had not wanted it, nor could they prevent it, and therefore they disclaimed responsibility for the matter and hid the tragedy under the cloak of observance. The comfortable prayers went up to the unlistening God in the chapel, and the tragedy disappeared from view as the small black bell rang out in the darkness signalling the end of the thought that should be given to the matter.

It was some time before I realised that the small Communist group which had been formed in the University had gone quietly out like unwanted visitors. They were now in my position on the outside. Many, ashamed of what the system had done and unable to comprehend the whole problem, had kept away from the agitated groups. I felt for them during this troubled time and would like to have seen them again to express my understanding of their problem. I mentioned this to George one day who retorted violently and with the limited vision that the sudden onset of war had left him.

"There is no understanding what they have done. They have left our dead rotting in the roads fighting for their power, they have left old and young alike completely powerless. You have feelings of sympathy for them. They deserve to be beaten into hell for what they have done."

In this I had my first initiation into real hate. The overpowering emotion that strikes at all, however vaguely connected.

"My leader and yours," I said, "were taken prisoner and beaten, and yet remained silent, and for them the problem is the same. Those who are their leaders are now being verbally crucified. They are perplexed as we are perplexed. They are suffering as we are suffering.

"Suffering!" he said. "Monsters like that can't suffer."

"They will suffer," I replied, "their ideals are shattered

130

and their leaders shamed. Their crucifixion, like ours, will go on through life, they are not without feeling."

He hurled abuse at them and I gave up the attempt at reasoning. I knew they would walk the precipice for the rest of their university career, and I knew the loneliness and the perplexity, and I walked away from that man feeling as though death itself were the only solution, the only state where these problems would be solved.

The students themselves made attempts at solutions. One group acquired a small battered bus and went off in a small band to do what they could. They went like saviours, young people who would have been called by any good cause but hardly knew what pain they would meet. I never saw that group again in the slouched freedom of the quadrangle, and they, like the tragedy that had beckoned them were soon forgotten. Perhaps the terror they had witnessed made them unable to take on the studies which then must have seemed so unimportant, or maybe it was that the bus, battered at the outset, never reached its journey's end, and they were too ashamed to return and tell the tale. Was the kingdom lost to Hungary for the want of a wheel, or perhaps because of someone who should have helped but was encumbered suddenly with some temporary love that ended wildly under a hayrick? Whatever the cause, Hungary lost the battle and we were forced into ignominious forgetfulness.

Later in the term the Communist students filtered back and were like men whom a great disaster had befallen which they could not believe. They were in the Common room one afternoon when I had forgotten part of the horror.

One young man called Colin sat with one leg swinging

on the table. A creased forehead reached a curl that taunted the lines of worry.

"Why change your allegiance now? How do we know what is true? We can never know the truth."

He was answered by another whose face was covered by hands that were risen in supplication for hearing.

"If it were so great an evil that they did we are effecting nothing by changing sides when the current is strong. If we lose our faith in the Party now what have we left? There is nothing else we can accept. Hold on now, even though the trouble seems insurmountable."

"We are twisted in a Machiavellian grip," another said. "It is impossible now to know what is right and wrong. We must cling on to the vision we had."

"What do you say, Sister?" The question was thrust out to me like a pointed spear. I was doubly outside them, a Christian who had been carrying ideals as they their troubles.

"Me," I said, "what can I offer you? It's the season of disillusionment."

"Which side is your God on?" They were taunting me now, asking the question to which I had no answer. In the net, cornered as I was, I said, "The side that can face God and declare that which they did was right. The side that can explain the shedding of all this blood. The side that is able to return the blood-smattered body of a son to a mother and feel it is justified. The man that can do this is on the right side." Later I prayed . . .

"My feebled-faced God hiding in the clouds, show your face and listen to my prayer. You who are the wiper away of ideals listen to me. Justify for me this wretched destruction of a country that wished to honour you, a country that wished to keep you in their politics and their schools, their whole lives. Yet it is they you have wiped out, they you have shattered in blood along the paving stones of the land that honoured and respected you. Pick up the bodies into eternal rest and terrify your enemies, throw them to one side as you did in the ages that are past. Listen to me God. We cannot understand you, we can hardly believe that You still exist. The pain of Your people is our pain, and the pain You suffered was our pain. Is it because You are the three in One that You can show so many different faces? My God I still try to believe in You. Help my unbelief my God."

I afterwards felt like Judas, but the prayer had gone up over the rotting bodies that had been mutilated and destroyed. I stood in that room before those people like a traitor. I was the symbol of ideals and the soul of convention and I mouthed answers I did not understand. I was enmeshed in a world of littleness when the world was being shaken by heroism. Clumsiness was losing Russia its supporters but I lost my God at that time because He continually smiled on the atrocities that were being committed. Theological theories were like so many balls of wool that I held in my hand. I could use them or throw them away, but they were unsuitable colours for the funeral life that shrouded the world at that time.

Disillusion walked through the halls of the University and invisible fingers beckoned me back on to the road of rules, and I hated it fiercely once again. There has never been anything that affected my life so much as the perplexity of that time. The coloured dress of the Hungarians appeared again and again to me splashed with the blood that was so uselessly shed. I wandered through the storm of that blood until the term ended, and I never lost sight

133

of the raped girls, the drunken soldiers, the disillusioned youth, the pathetic mothers, and the God carefully laughing down on His world from the clouds.

"Christ scourged at the pillar have mercy on us, tortured Christ remember your pains, Mater Dolorosa succour them!"

15

WHEN THE term ended the nuns who were study-
ing in the University and in the various colleges
returned to the convent. One morning the Mother
Superior sent for me.

"Sister," she said, "I have arranged for you to have a
rest in the . . ." Before she could finish the sentence I knew
I was going back to the walls that had confined me so
fiercely before I went to the University.

"I'm quite well, Mother," I said. "I don't need a rest,
I have work I must do."

"Take your books with you and go where the Good God
sees fit to send you." As she said this she handed me a small
purse with the fare for the journey wrapped safely in it.
I automatically stretched out my hand for the purse, protesting all the time that I wanted to stay where I was.
There was an air of outraged horror surrounding her.

"It is not a case of what you want, but a question of
your obedience, and you must go when you are told."

We went that same day, Sister Josephine and I. We
neither of us dared to express the panic we felt, but com-
municated it to each other on the journey. We took a bus
from the city. Such an outing would have thrilled us but

for the destination that confronted us at our journey's end. I began to wish the journey would last for ever, then selfishly and childishly hope that the bus would crash and we would end in hospital. The bus continued skilfully along the jagged roads, and led us to the convent that arose in the distance like an internment camp. We went like beaten prisoners with no rights and no support. We had hardly spoken to one another. Sister Josephine looked out of the window, and I thought about the convent and my past unhappy experiences in the place.

We arrived there and acted as a tragic-comic showpiece for the old nuns who had never left the convent in twenty years. We were for them sinister and threatening voices from a world that I had chosen to leave. Yet we reminded them that their old age was secured and that the convent would go on. They were like embittered grandmothers who were glad to see the line continue but despised the pretensions of the young, whom indirectly they had caused to be born.

The Mother Superior met us with clammy hand and badly concealed authority. In the main convent from which we had come the Superiors were usually too busy or too wise to enforce petty restrictions and harsh authoritarianism.

Almost at once we were given our rooms which were much smaller than those to which we had grown accustomed. There was room for a bed and nothing else. There was no chair or table, and a harsh black crucifix decorated the white wall. Like a monstrous spider it sprawled over the whitewashed brick. The room shrieked claustrophobia. I knew at once that I would be unable to sleep there.

"Mother Superior, I am not able to sleep in a room where the ceiling is so low and the atmosphere so cramped."

"Well, Sister, the young nuns these days are changing. Is it hotel accommodation you're wanting?" Her lapse into the Irish colloquialism irritated me, but I showed no emotion.

"I know I won't be able to sleep there, I have claustrophobia."

"What a variety of illnesses there are today, Sister. A name for everything. That's what's happening, names, names, and then special consideration and relaxation of the rules. No, Sister, this is your room and you must sleep here. This is your cross and you must bear it." Smiling her brisk smile she left the room, pressing the palms of her hands closely together as though she were crushing my writhing body in between her grip.

I went first to the Community room that was almost as bare as the bedroom. I was given a drawer in which to place my few belongings.

The bell for the night prayers rang out and we jostled one another in the narrow corridor in order to be there in time. We pretended the magnificence of the city convent, but the voices, most of them wearied with age and routine, sent up a shallow cry in the night gloom.

After prayers there was the silent meal, and later the recreation period. The gloom, the ever-present restriction, and the harsh voice of the Superior made the hour much more difficult than the hour of recreation in the Novitiate. The old nuns sat shoulder hunched over their sewing, age and submission kept them quiet. The Superior's voice scraped in the awkward silence.

"Sister, why don't you sing for us?"

"I can't sing, Mother, nor can Sister Josephine."

"A small duet won't hurt you at all, and it will be nice for the older nuns."

My mouth was dry and my hands were marking the sewing with their sweat.

"I just can't."

"Sister, you really must start practising to do as you're told. Don't spoil the recreation atmosphere with your sulking."

" 'The Spinning Wheel' is a song I love," one of the old nuns said.

We started the song. Anything for peace I thought. My eyes stung with the humiliation and my voice cracked on until finally the dryness forced me to stop. I did not dare to look at Sister Josephine, and looked hard at my sewing. The Community that was withering with age clapped gently, and we were left alone for the rest of the hour.

At the end of the period the Mother Superior asked Sister Josephine if she would undertake the period of "night caller" with me on alternate nights. This meant that we had to ensure that the doors were locked and the hens that were kept in a small hen-coop in the back yard shut up for the night.

I hated the dark and decided to take my turn first and finish the day that was already so painful with this last act of submission. The blackness of the night always reminded me of death. It suddenly came from nowhere, a black box of evil awaiting me with Plutonian grasp, and there was no Orpheus to whistle me back to the upper regions. I could die in that evil cloak and lie in Hades and there would be no one to look for me. No one to whom my disappearance would matter. This fear of non-existence followed me perpetually, since God seemed so far away and so indecisive, and the nights so dark.

I went into the chicken yard and walked the dark path, clutching the keys tightly in my hand. They were my symbol of freedom and security. There was a movement behind me. I was too frightened to go or to stay. The Superior was standing there, white faced like the Lapland witch, as the hens crowed and cooed their way to sleep. An old proverb was going through my mind but I could not remember what it was. I was really afraid, and in my fear I unlatched the hen-coop and the hens rushed to me as though protecting me. The black hens moved near the Mother Superior, they were like jaunty devils rushing round the small world. The wind began to blow, and to get away from the blast and the deep searching eyes of the Superior, I rushed into the house. I was trembling in every part of my body, and yet the nun had said nothing, I had no complaint to make that would be reasonable. Why was she there? I wondered, in the cold garden, wordless and searching?

I made my way to the tiny room that had been allotted to me, the small square part of the house where I was to have the rest I had been ordered to take. The kennelled atmosphere choked me, and I stood in the room like a chained dog. I was once again separated from all that I respected and understood. I could not voice my opinion to anyone who would view it with sympathy. I was lonely as I had never before been lonely. My life had erupted before me and there was nothing I could do. My friends were forcibly removed and I was to be forced into a companionship with people who seemed so old that it was difficult to imagine they had ever been young. The generation in which they had been young was so different that even if they could have remembered those days their feelings would have been removed from anything I was feeling.

The night was completely dark in that room. The lights were switched off at the main and I could do nothing to alleviate the darkness. Swallowed up by this and the crushing walls I lay in the bed hunched and tense, straining in the darkness to see the whiteness of the sheet that made the room less like a well. In the end I slept, and every night that followed I slept after the first fearful hour. There were many nights that I lay and looked, without flinching, at the door. Was it because it was the way to escape, or the entrance by which whatever I feared could enter? I never knew, but I began to watch that door night after night. The last thing I saw was the back of the door with my black cloak hanging like a criminal over the door-knob.

Opposite my room was the white wall of the narrow corridor. The other rooms lay alongside mine, but there was only a wall opposite.

One morning, before the early dawn had come, I awoke in the corridor, awakened perhaps by my own banging and shouting. The convent was completely still, and the wall white and indifferent. For five nights after this I awoke banging against the white tomb that lay across the corridor from my room. The nightmares of my childhood had come back.

Night after night I was hemmed into the bus queue, I was rooted to the ground like a magical tree, nothing could move me. I ran in blind alleys, chased like a hunted deer, and fleetness was of no avail because they were after me. I never saw them but they chased me with a fearful persistency. Sometimes I was tethered in the garden, and when I tried to escape the branches of the tree enveloped me. In a laundry I was wrapped in a sheet and struggling against the winding. I choked, they were around me coiling, coiling. Hands from nowhere searched for me, and I ran in my dreams like a criminal. I had become the hanging prisoner on the door. I choked as though I were being hanged. I sweated as though the last moments had come.

I was no longer myself but a hunted animal for whom there was no refuge. Often I was a prisoner and the wire mesh surrounded me. I dwelt in the depths of darkness and there was no light.

In the daylight I thought of the dreams and dismissed them in the sunlight. After every day of sunlight there was the night. I spent the day searching for God in the hope that His light might enlighten the night. He had come as the Light of the world, and I was terrified of the darkness He had created. I served Him and devoted my life to His cause, but every night He switched on the darkness as I groped.

In the end I returned to the Superior's room and demanded that I share a big room with another nun.

"Your room has been allotted to you, Sister, and you must make the best of it. In religion we don't choose our rooms any more than we do our companions."

I tried to talk but I couldn't explain about the hunters or the winding sheets. I suffered this alone. I was alone.

"You are alone, totally alone except for God now," I said to myself.

"Can you tell me where He is now?" a voice said to me. "Hiding or asleep, He is just trying me out."

I did not believe the story I had made up for myself. I began to wonder again about the whole of life. Why had we been born? Was there never to be any joy, was it all to be pain?

One night, half asleep and half awake, I dreamt of dictators and their death warrants. I remembered Hungary, I remembered the Jews. I saw clearly before me a knife, a common kitchen knife, as the salvation. I would rid the house of the tyrant. I would clear the house of dictators. I would disperse the enemy. In the daylight when I was in the kitchen I saw the knife and plunged it, cruelly and without cause, into the harmless sack of potatoes, and felt sick when it touched the flesh of the round brown bodies within.

The night came again and the darkness fell, and I dreamt as I always dreamt in that room. This time the dream was more curious. I was creeping, in my dream, quietly and without fear, out of the window, along the roof and down on to the street on my way to freedom. The convent began to move into the distance.

I was free of the room that had held me captive, that had smothered me without thought, that had hidden life from me, that had enclosed me in the country of lost hope and unsafe power. Free! I was free! I could breathe in a new way, in a way that I had forgotten. I was alone. At last I had thrown off the enemy. There was no need of death. There was no need to act as saviour. I could get back to the city convent as a refugee. I had left everything in the tiny prison, I needed nothing, just safety and companionship. There was new hope where I was going, the possibility of understanding. There was to be no blood shed.

In the happy sleep of release I had seen myself talking in the big convent to the Superiors, who were all wise. They understood the small rooms and the darkness of the closed chicken-coop. They would not leave me sinking in the quagmire, they would not leave me in the dark. They would hold back the itching hand that had sought to bring about the wrath of God. They knew the terrors of acting as God. They would never let me wash my hands in the blood of the insane. There was no peace to be gained in that way. I dreamed of a girl running through the streams that had surrounded the Irish house of my early childhood. The blood trailed in and around the room. I was completely surrounded by the blood.

I cried for the freedom with the voice of the book of Samuel, "If I have found favour in thine eyes let me get away." From Job the comfort of the hopeless, "Terrors take hold of him as waters, a tempest stealeth him away in the night." The tempest had come to the door. They were crying for me to come, these nymphs of blood were wailing their tune of sadness. I joined them like the lonely sparrow in the penitential psalm. I was alone as he on the housetop. The sparrow ran into the dream and escaped, it seemed to me, over the houses. A new road had been made by the roofs that co-operated and sympathised with me. They would carry me, I was sure, out of the small convent, the dark smoke would shield me, and freely and in freedom I would return to the city that held in the grime the salvation that I sought.

It was the cold and the movement that had wakened me. I felt the hand of capture on the wrist, the helping hand that brought me in again into the house that seemed so like a prison. I was awake. There was no city convent. The friendly hand became recognised, the white hand of help and surrender was passed out of the window. I had been brought back from the rooftop. I was the sparrow, but there was no safety there. My friend who had heard my wall-like scrabbling knew this and brought me back again into the silent convent.

The cup of tea, the warm hand of the friend and the alleviation of the darkness of the night helped me and I fell again into a fitful sleep that was pierced at times by the sharp-bladed knife.

The next day the Superior sent for me. She was sitting in her chair and waited for me to kneel. Her whole body spoke disapproval, and her questions were hurtled fiercely and harshly.

"What is the meaning of attracting attention to yourself, Sister? What good do you think it will do? Are you trying to blackmail me into changing your room?"

"No, Mother," I said. "I couldn't help it, I was asleep."

"Asleep! Crawling around the roof tops like a tom cat. Asleep! You sleep in your bed and in the room I have given to you. I am speaking to Mother Provincial this morning and I will ask her what she thinks of your escapade?"

"Do that," I blurted. "She will believe me."

"Believe you, Sister? There is nothing to be believed except the truth which is evident. You have been attention seeking ever since you put your foot through the door. She knows well your inability to accept the arrangements that have been made for you. You were unwilling to come here, and you think by these means you can escape your duty. You will speak your fault tonight, Sister, and ask forgiveness from the Community for causing a disturbance in the night after the Great Silence."

"I won't, Mother. I can't. The days when I told untruths for the sake of humility are past. I am not responsible for what I have done in my sleep. It is wrong to ask pardon for that as though I had done it deliberately. I have apologised to the Sister whom I awoke, there is nothing left for me to say."

"You will do as you are told, and now you may go, Sister." I was dismissed, and held the door in my hand. Controlling myself I closed it quietly.

I had to get away, of this I was sure, yet I would not now be so welcome in the convent where previously I had been accepted. I had nothing to offer, I could not cover up my defects with the rags of past service. I was young and new, and as such came to the Community as a beggar. I had no proof of service.

There was one thing of which I was sure. I would not speak my fault that evening. I could hold out against that. I did, and nothing more was said, but the gloom of the night chapel was followed by the darkness, and then the dark of the room. The dreams of the sleep and the sweat of the fear came again and I lay there, chased and hunted, awaiting the day of liberation, waiting for the dividing of the waters, waiting for the path to be cleared. I waited, and eventually the waiting ended, and I returned to the city.

16

THE TROUBLES that came at this time were as a wide breaking of the waters. My sorrow was carried on the wind and lost in the cloud of desolation that surrounded the city convent. I came back to the city and began again to prepare for the coming term.

I did not recover my former equilibrium and went back to the University ill prepared for the term that was to come. The city house now seemed too big. I was lost in the innumerable rooms and the impersonal atmosphere that had seemed so desirable during my captivity. Suddenly I feared the space, there seemed always some unknown danger lurking around the corner. The corridors seemed to be of incredible width, and to pass from one to the other was becoming a task in itself.

Passing the tiny slum dwellings on the way to the University I was surrounded by unrecognisable new fears that came and went as I walked. As soon as I had arrived safely I began at once to dread the walk out again into the wide roads. The sweat poured from my body in a terrible anticipation. I walked again and again the Calvaried Hill. I saw the small dirty houses no longer as homes of the poor I knew and loved. Now they seemed a dishevelled enemy who were grouped around the doorways and looked as I passed, and whispered as I went. They stood in their dirt like judges in condemnation, their clothes simply the customary cloth of their dwelling, but their look conveyed the word of disapproval about which I wondered as I walked. They seemed like giants who had come unmasked out of the fairy tale book that had sat for many years harmlessly on the edge of the bookcase in my home.

I changed my route to the University, but others were there, strangers. They looked at me, a foreigner who walked the immense roads exposed to all the dangers that came in from the highway over which I had no authority.

I had one friend who was always there whatever route I took—an old gum-sucking figure of eighty years, bedraggled by the time spent in the grime that had embedded itself into his old face. He had smiled always as I passed. He was for me a sentry that stood at the gate. My smile of recognition was the pass into the world I formerly had left. He saw and smiled, and moved along in his shuffling life.

One day, when the air sparkled with expectation, and the children, barefooted, with the crumbling bread of their houses held between their teeth, greeted me with the usual smirk and run, I walked quietly along the accustomed road. They did not mind the nuns, they came each day like the milkman and the paper boy to the houses of those whose parents were working. As long as they were not those who begged the children were allowed to smile at them. For those who begged the technique was very different. They ran to warn the mothers who smoked the cigarette ends behind the curled smoke of the cooker, and under the shade of their net wrapped hair. The dirtied nails on these occasions closed the door that served as a bridge between the sounds of the road and the sound of the human quarrelling which, even in these deprived quarters, was confined as far as possible to the five houses that surrounded their sulky terraced lines. These houses were, for the running bread-fed children, the haven of peace and the suppliers of needs. They skipped the last steps of the pavement as we came along. They pushed the bread safely into the mouth that accepted this substitute breast in the hour of danger. They looked out of eyes already dirtied with the roughness of the slum. They were interested in the black groups that shone with unusual cleanliness.

Yet on this morning my toothless sentry did not come out of the doorway that blinked in the sunshine. I had wondered about him, and his disappearance made the road wider and the way even more uneasy. I had missed his hand at the cap which did not resent the touch. The cap or the man, I was never sure, gave me admission. This morning there was no admission. There was no guard on duty, no welcome, no repulse. I passed through the gates of his kingdom without thought, without recognition. I was neither friend nor enemy to the children. I was again a nonentity. They did not heed or need me.

The passing of his bronchial welcome came with sharpness, and I felt sad during the day. The fear of the wide spaces began to fade and I was eager for the walk home. I was determined to find the old man. The rain had come with a new strength that was not usual. The road where the old man lived was like the Stygian waters, but the boatman was not there to greet me. Charon, with the stern face and ever chewing gums, had gone into oblivion behind drawn blinds.

The children who played as ever on the street paid no attention to the silent sentry. They coursed around the wet ground and caught each other as they slipped. They were alive. In such a slum it was the living who mattered. They had impoverished policies for the dead, and the careful burials were symbolic of the needs of the living. They made no fuss about the patriarchal passing. The eighty years of striving were recognised in the passing of the milk stout, but the contest of the immortal soul was fought out between God and the octogenarian who tried to remember the misdeeds of the eighteen year old youth who to him now must seem never to have existed. He was dead, the family gathered the insurance, and I walked to the convent with the tired steps and a new realisation of the world to come. His passing did for me what the theology lessons had never done. They had taught me about the doctrine of immortality and the ever rising choirs of angels, yet there had never, until this time, been for me a true realisation of death. There was no need of theology, death was simply the going, the non-existence, the emptiness of a grey pavement in the early morning. He was the first of my secular friends to die and, as such, made the greatest impact.

17

THE TERM continued without the old man, and the examinations began to be spoken of again. There was serenity and happiness in the convent and we worked and walked every day. We were happy in each other's company. We encouraged each other to work, and consoled each other when the fear of failure overcame us. We were apart from the rest of the students and we had finally persuaded ourselves to accept this. Yet for me the remembrance of the country convent remained. We were all, after the examination, destined for another holiday in the closed confines.

Night after night I saw the little convent and the narrow room that, more and more for me, became the boxlike symbol of my death. I wondered how I could explain to the Mother Provincial who in her kindness organised the holidays.

As I thought about the coming holidays the rooms in the convent began to assume for me the most extraordinary shapes. I wandered from room to room seeking relief. The only place where I could find peace was the quadrangle of the University that was large and, at the same time, enclosed. I needed the closed environment and, at the same time, the space.

One day, making my way without the other nuns, I tried to cross the road that led from the Faculty of Arts to the Science block. It was completely impossible, as difficult as crossing the Lethe without the dust, and the heavenly roads without the death. I waited at the roadside like a hunted animal. Clutching my black bag I hovered around the circled road that gleamed with the whiteness of a new soul. The way was untrammelled, the road, like my choice, was clear. I had simply to walk, but I could not. I prayed for the other nuns to come, and in their strength I hoped to find power to cross the road which had suddenly become my enemy. They did not come, and the road would not narrow, and I waited. I stood on the roadside like a lonely tinker who had lost his caravan in a disaster. Finally, like the remains of a defeated army I shamefully withdrew my steps back to the building from which I had come. I was afraid, and could do nothing but pick up my shame and huddle it to myself. I heard the hooting traffic and the black cars moving like sightful owls as a background to my retreat. I recalled, in this moment of shame, an incident in my childhood.

I had, as a tiny child, feared to cross the road where the gipsy caravan had made its home. Then, the alternative to the admission of failure, was to seek the help of the non-Catholic minister. In my world of all or nothing Catholicism, the non-Catholic hierarchy was as dreadful as the devil. On that day I had to choose between the non-Catholic canon and the gipsies, and I had chosen the canon. I felt secure as I walked up his neat path. A man who had so tidy a garden could not, I thought, be evil. If he surrounded himself with flowers, and had cast out the weeds who were the sworn friends of the devil, surely I would be safe.

Today there was for me no comfortable canon. There was no one to place their warm hands in mine and take me past the enemy. I remembered the scholarly canon with affection, he who had long since gone and settled finally the theological differences that had made me afraid in the bygone days of the lost childhood. Now I had to make my own decisions. I had to accept defeat, if defeat it was. The choice was mine and had to be made.

When I returned to the library I knew I had been defeated. I listened to the assistants as they chatted to the students.

"See you then tonight."

"Maybe, if you're lucky. A hop isn't everyone's cup of tea."

A stamp of the book and the purpled number bespoke the future love between the two.

"Can I help you, Sister?"

She must be a Catholic. It was only the Catholics who used that tone. Respect, inbred from childhood days, came in waves over the counter.

"No, no I'm just waiting for the others."

Why, I thought, can we never say what we mean? "Librarian assistant," I wanted to say, "I am terrified of the road. I cannot get across. It is like the passage between life and death for me. Hold my hand as I go. Walk a little with me until I have crossed the river. Take my hand in the darkness, guide me to safety. I am blind and wandering and alone, guide me and support me."

I said nothing, and I have been glad many times that the mind does not wholly disregard the future. I could never have gone there again if I had said what I was thinking, but there was no need to feel ashamed. The control which they had instilled in me during the Novitiate and since could not be overcome so easily, and I passed out of that torment without embarrassing the assistant who stamped the books as though she were blotting out the weakness I felt.

I waited there some time. I eventually found the courage to move again.

"Good-bye, Sister," the voice said.

The purpled love seemed to look at me with some perplexity.

"Good-bye."

Sometimes these words seem to me to hold all time. They are dividing lines between life and death, work and play, illness and health, they are so final. They are terrifying in their intensity, and yet we shout them down the stairs and along the road. Sometimes they are the final words of separation, they are sometimes the closing moment in the happiness of life. The end of joy and the beginning of sadness and the beginning of joy. The death of sin or the seed of infidelity. To me, that day, they were all of these things. I knew they were a prologue to a long separation of everything I loved.

I wandered along the corridor that led to the grounds. Where am I going? There was no voice to answer, "Get back, get back to safety, to the love imprinted in the book. Get back to the death that surrounds the words, whatever you do, get back."

I went back, because for me then there was no way out.

"Back again, Sister?"

I was like a moth that had flitted out and then back to feed a little longer on the dead articles that lay there, that were now my only protection in the death called life.

153

Suddenly it was no longer the confined walls that worried, but the ever increasing space. The sea surrounded me, deafening me, drowning me. Everything was wide, terrifying, moving, moving. I remembered the gulls, who now seemed to be all around me, crying, shrieking, mourning their life of freedom. The light in the room faded, and the blackness came. The howling cry of the gulls penetrated my ears and I felt weak. The light was going. In the daytime the light was moving. Two nights in that one day. There was no one to help me, no one to call my name. Call my name, for God's sake call my name! The sea is coming into my soul, and the knowledge of who I am is going from me. The voices of the children whom I had known were all around me shouting their freedom.

"Throw the ball, Sister, move along, it's my turn, mind the cracks, keep silence."

The screaming of the birds seemed now to encompass me and I fought desperately to escape from the morass in which I found myself.

I sat and waited for the nuns to come, but their coming was like the morning of a sleepless night. The clock moved in the rounded time with its baby face of innocence. I sat in the shadow of the hand that clicked into the afternoon that was a continuation of the terrible morning. They did not come. The clock chimed out the half hourly warnings of passing life. It turned on its circled way without consideration. The golden face despised me and clucked its tongue disapprovingly, and then moved on with its work. I was doing nothing, the time for hope had shivered around the clock, and hopelessly life passed from quarter to quarter. I could see the passing of the whole, and heard in every chime a death knell warning me of my torpor.

They did not come. Yet I could not believe it possible

that the last anchor had gone. The sea was overcoming me, I was drowning in the library of browning books. They were surrounding me, overcoming me, changing from friend to enemy. They had no affection for me, like the non-returning friends they did not care.

I moved at last from the library. I walked again on to the quadrangle that led to the road. I had no hope of transport and yet I must move, I could not wait for ever like Penelope, and there was no web in which I could entwine myself, no father-in-law to act as my protector, my excuse, my refuge.

The road came again into my view, and I walked, crippled with the terror. I moved on the invisible sticks that supported me so crudely. They were so spindle-shaped, and I feared I would collapse as I moved away from one security into another.

A small dog moved with closed eyes and rushed without care on to the road. Overcome by the need to protect him I moved instinctively to bring him back into my security of grey paving stones. The yelp that he gave startled me, and I moved aside sharply from his young avenging teeth. He thrust them out as the cars swerved to miss us both. We crossed the road together.

Once across I made the journey home. I kept near the wall side as I walked, always aware that the wall was there to protect me. The noise of the traffic came like the cry of wild animals. They want to trap me, I thought, to track me down on the grey paving stones. They could not let me move in safety. They pranced around me, filling me with new fears. They rushed at me, and at the moment of the kill they halted on oiled hoofs and well trained paws. They did not kill me. They would not let the pain pass so easily. They had seen that I had tried to escape. Like a frightened animal they had seen me go. They did not understand the battles that had taken place. They could not, in their shiny blackness of new power on the highway, comprehend my loneliness. They could not understand the length of the journey that I had walked without help. They moved with shining ease across the land that had been so difficult for me to cross. How could they know my weariness? I had walked like an unwilling hitcher across an unknown world, and had found the people not only unfriendly but menacing. The land itself had risen up against me. I cried out for the shelter of a haystack to protect me in the hateful noon heat. Yet the cars still came swerving and screaming like the gulls who had been my friends. They came near and then changed their intention. They would not kill me, they enjoyed the game too much.

As I turned the corner of the street that I had seen so often, and yet had never really noticed, I realised the journey was ending, that the crowds of friends I had left in the early morning were waiting there. They would not understand yet they would be there. They would protect me from the new enemy that had come so suddenly out of the grey road that had always before been so friendly to me. The little road had never, until this day, harmed me. Always, like a faithful friend, it had led me to the University and brought me back each night. I had never feared the road before, and now I could not understand how I had ever trusted so strange a friend. How could enemies change so rapidly? How could Jesus have turned against Judas, and he against Christ? I had never understood this, and I had feared always this terrible treachery. When I crossed the convent threshold how would I know that the others had not changed to me as had those in the University? Would they leave me to battle out what must be, I was sure, the last battle? What was the battle for? Who were the enemy? We prance along in our life continually fighting the enemy whom we do not even know. I had finished. I had not sufficient strength to find out who the enemy was. I would end it all.

I remembered the gas stoves in the kitchen. They were there with their perfume of death and their flickering flame to light the way. During all the battles I had forgotten them. I would defeat the enemy, I would fool the pain that had surrounded me.

I remember it now. I walked quite quickly along the dark corridor that led to the kitchen. It was so clean, clinical like a hospital, and there was no one there. Pans reflecting my desperation shone with amazing purity. The stoves were there. Death lay inside their doors, poison in their arms, and I welcomed it.

I never thought of death at that moment or feared it, the question of how to use the gas and to keep out the air confused me and I thought about this. I bent towards the door of the oven and it was awkward. That is all I can remember about my death trap.

I was kneeling on the floor, always hunched and kneeling. The last gesture to the life that ruled me, the last obeisance to the majesty that had kept me there.

Dried meat smells greeted and nauseated me, and then the gas, effortlessly and sweetly, streaming into my nose and then into my head. Then the feeling of relaxation, sleepiness. The feeling that all the loads were being placed finally on the floor. Even the weight seemed to go out of my body and I floated, up and up, breathing out life and inhaling death.

18

I WAS TAKEN to the hospital and later back to the convent. There the voices were softer than I had ever heard them. I tried to tell them about the animals who had gone screeching by. They could not understand and their responses hardly ever varied.

"Take it easy now, forget the whole thing."

Forget the whole thing! I had almost shaken off the animals, I had stretched out of the world but was pulled back by their hands, and for what? Why? They could not even begin to understand.

It was a few days later that I noticed the white screens. They had cut me off now, not only from the world but the convent life. People appeared from the outside of the curtain as though entering a stage. I had a world that belonged only to me. They moved from their sphere into mine, trying all the time to comprehend.

Sister Josephine who had been in the small convent came every day.

"Do you want to talk about it, Sister?"

"Talk," I said, "about what? About what has brought me here? About the action that makes them whisper in corners? I don't want to talk. When I wanted to talk they wouldn't allow it, and now that there is nothing to say they want you to make me talk. When you go out of here the Superior will send for you to tell her all we said."

She went out quietly, and I will never know why I was so harsh. I didn't feel bitter, I simply felt nothing. So much of nothing surrounded me. I was wading in it day after day. Strangled by it, swallowed by it, I was bitter, more bitter at that moment than I can remember.

I lay there remembering the University. The grey spires that leered up towards the sky, and the towers that looked like devils on the end of a lollipop stick. I saw the inside of the church, grey, so very grey and dark, with the white smoke of the incense coiling up alone to God, pale and frightened.

I thought then of the garden leaves. Why I don't know, but I saw them littered on the ground waiting to be trampled into the earth so that they might rise again. The trees had sacrificed them to the ground as a graceful gift. Every leaf that fell had my pity, it was borne to the ground at the whim of the branch. Trampling armies of feet would close them in the earth, and the eyes of the people to whom the feet belonged would in turn admire the plants that came from the leaves in another season. Seasoned and circled we have our life, trampled and crushed it rises again. A new form takes up the tired image and recreates, and the uselessness of the one passes as the source of the next.

With the garden the life came back. Gulls were everywhere, their cry joined with the wildness of the waves and their noise came to me in the screened off existence. As always they moved away in freedom, they would not be trampled, nothing would hold them, neither life nor death, sickness or despair. They flew away.

I slept then and the dreams came in over the screen.

159

There was nothing that could keep the dreams out of my new world. The heat was tropical. Everywhere a blistering sun scorched me, and a hand moved in the bed. The hand of Sister Angela was everywhere in the bed. The plucking hand came back, back, back, so close to me. It had come to strangle me and moved nearer and nearer. I tried to throw it out of the bed. It was there, refusing to go, Sister Angela's hand, white and blue, but searching with such purpose, searching for me. The enemy had come into the camp. Who had let it in, who refused to let me know of the power of a white hand, the hand that had rotted in the grave, the young hand suddenly old and frightening?

I awoke as suddenly as I had slept and found my hand numb and imprisoned by my tortured body. My own weight had brought back Sister Angela's hand. I was desperately throwing my own hand from the bed.

The darkness was everywhere. I needed the light to switch off the agony of the dream. I screamed aloud and the Infirmarian came and found the switch, and order came into the room almost as she made the movement towards the switch.

She had set her face against God, I thought. The Maker of dark and light is baffled by the switch.

"He is thwarted by the switch," I said.

"Would you like a drink, Sister?" she held out a cup tentatively.

"Day and night have gone out of life," I was so desperately trying to explain but her reply of "Would you take a tablet with the drink?" made me realise it was quite impossible.

"Try not to talk, Sister." She held out a drink and tablet.

"It will send me back to the ring."

"It will give you a good sleep, Sister, and that's what you need."

I was dismissed for the second round, encircled by the drug I was entangled by the ropes and it all started again. I was no prize fighter, I was nothing. The nothing was coming back like a friend who had left me for a short time. It was coming back, back into the bed. The nights were long and were shortened but made more fearful by the tablet. The doctor came the next day.

"How are we today, Sister?" He had a tight face and forced cheerfulness. His lips were tight, and his mouth one of the smallest I have ever seen on a man. The kind of lips an orphan should have. A mouth that had never taken in love in the early days. He was neat, careful in what he said and what he did. He carried his medical bag as though he were a magician carrying spells. He was hearty, and the words seemed to burst out of his mouth as though raping the aperture. Rounded in a tight exactness he looked at me. Black hair oiled into the right and the left and a straight parting made for the thoroughfare of the world. "Don't touch me," it said, "walk right through." It had, as well. Life had walked right past him. He never suffered and was never happy. He made money and bought oil for his hair and clothes for his middle-class body, and thought of nothing. He was clean, he had walked clean through the world. He was unbent by the pain, he did not even recognise it. He phrased all his questions in the plural as though he were fearful to admit there were things that one suffered completely on one's own. He came and went, and I never saw further than the parting where the grey was beginning. There was never any more experience to draw on. He might as well have inspected the sheets. I was a body, a patient whom he did not really understand, and indeed whom he was fearful of understanding.

The days passed suddenly and I wanted to rejoin the other nuns. I wanted to hear them breathe in the darkness. I wanted to be sustained by the breath that arose in the stillness of the sleeping room.

When the Superior came to see me on her evening call I told her what I wanted.

"Are you quite ready yet, Sister? Isn't it perhaps a bit too soon?"

"I want to hear them, Mother, the chorus of their breath rising in the night. When I cannot sleep I listen to them and I know I am alive. Otherwise I am dead, my body deserts my mind and I lie there waiting for the morning light that will so soon again turn into the depth that is night."

"Very well, Sister, I will mention it to the Infirmarian and we will see what we can do. There is no point in lying here being lonely."

"It isn't that I am lonely, but there is a blackness, a nothingness in the middle of my stomach. We are all so lonely there is nothing that can move it. The darkness accentuates it, but it is always there. There, there, when there is nothing to be done. It begins when we are born, Mother Superior. When we fight out our lives in their first hour we alienate the world because we have won the battle against death. I want to hear the breathing not to remove my loneliness but to know that the blackness of death has not come. To know we are alive."

A few days later I went back to the dormitory. It was exactly the same as it had always been and yet it seemed different to me. I was looking with new eyes at a well-known scene. The atmosphere was strange and I felt like an exile.

I went to my own corner where the bed stood white and blue in the daylight as though the sky had fallen into the room. I was at last enfolded in the sheets that might have been used for the winding. Alive, completely alive I looked at the room and waited for the night.

After the waiting the night came and I had to accustom myself to the breathing of the others. I had forgotten it and yet longed for it, and then the noise annoyed me. They lay there dreaming of what had passed in the day, and I, who had no dreams to remember but the white and blue nothingness, listened to their hymn. The paper, patterned into the ceiling, looked abused and forgotten. Their breathing became noisier and more violent, and for me the sleeplessness more apparent.

Suddenly, and without warning, I wanted the light and the Infirmarian with her magic arm. I was afraid of disturbing the others who had to rise in the morning when the bell rang loudly at six. I lay there. In the darkness I saw the pictures on the ceiling changing, bearing down on me, covering me with circles of horrified fear. Without mercy the dreams came back in my wakefulness. The knife moved in the darkness. Suddenly they were all coming again, the dreams, the people, the fears, the horrors of the years of confinement. The night was celebrating its darkness, the devil swung his tail as I lay there without moving. Don't move, I thought, don't move and they won't see you, do nothing and the moment will pass. But it never moved. The lid of a huge box opened and it seemed they tried to put me inside. The sides were black and the depth was out of my sight. Railings were erected round it. Everywhere there were railings surrounded by white bodies. The darkness was everywhere. I needed the light. It became my only thought and my only hope.

The lamp swayed above, disturbed by the breeze that came from the open window. I couldn't touch it nor make it light. I had no power at all, there was no way of escape. I was caught finally and at last. I saw the devil on the cushion on the chair. He moved when I sat up to look at him. He was disguised as the cover, and then leered from the ceiling. When I had touched the cushion the green silk made itself known to me. The mouth was open and the smile came from above. They have come for me, now at last they have found me. I am alone, completely alone, surrounded by friends and they are coming. Devils were everywhere. The ceiling brought them down like a service lift. The lamp swayed with their strength and in fear. I saw Christ swaying out His life on the hill of Calvary, a wisp in the air, a flotsam on the hill. I prayed to Him, but He did not come. He had slunk under the coverlet. He was no match for the devil.

"Christ," I prayed. "Protect me. Come out from the cover, body-bent God, bastard born Son of sin, protect me. Cover me in the danger. Paraclete spread your wings. Christ of the swaying hill protect me. Mary, mother of the following roadside, give your protection. Mother of Christ give me transport."

The lamp swayed above me. Christ did not listen, and the sound of the sleepers filled the room. The light, which hung like a reluctant star, would not shine, and the figure of Christ appeared, timid and frightened. One calvary was enough. God Christ would not involve Himself in another episode. I was alone this time, finally and completely. The devil would go when the dawn came, but I could not wait for the hours to pass. I needed the light. If I held the light in my arms all would pass. The devil's army suddenly changed to green. Everything in the room was green, like the slime on a pond, and I was drowning in the mass of slime. I wanted the light in my arms, to hold it fast for ever. It was life to me. Clinging to it I thought I would never die, there would be an end to darkness if I could control the light. To defeat the devil would be possible with the light, and only the light would defeat him. I would beat him to the ground, I would drive him from the cushion and blot out the smiling ceiling. With one flash of the light the bedraggled night that sold my safety would disappear.

They slept all the time. The others were sleeping, dreaming dreams I would never dream. I suffered this time on my own. I could not awaken them. They were unaware of the hens from the coop, of the knife that would split their neck, of the wire that hedged them in. They slept on unaware of what was happening. They were hidden in their world of dreams. The hours that made the reality bearable were now for me more agonising than the reality itself.

The lamp was still swaying and since the breeze was still blowing, the sleepers still sleeping, and the traffic still chugging on I knew I was alive and that the light would help me. It was the light itself that I wanted to hold in my arms and thus to blot out the night. The lamp swung, enraptured by the breeze, in the room of darkness. Aloud I said, "I want the light." My voice must have woken the others because they turned in restful sleep and began to rise up in their beds. Their heads were white in the darkness, the nightcaps made them look like ghosts. They were more unreal than ever. Just to touch the lamp, to know it was there, just to feel the reality.

It hung in the black room, jeering with its power. It became for me God the Maker of light and dark, and I had no control over it where I lay. I stretched toward it while the white faces of the novices turned toward me, while the white heads bobbed up and down like so many genuflections as the God-like lamp came down into the world of people. I stood in the swaying bed and held, for the first time, the light in my arms. The lamp fell into the room without beginning or end. Threaded to the ceiling as it was I heard the wrench as if God Himself had dropped into the life of human beings. It seemed as though He were forced suddenly to feel our feelings, to have the thread of life broken. The shattered Godhead fell into the bed that caved into a hollow with fear. I fell, holding God, the light, the beginning and end of the world. The uterine ripping succeeded in bringing the Maker of light into the world, but such earthly pressure forced only further darkness and total loss of hope into the dark room.

The hand I dreaded had come back, I could see the white hand moving slowly along the bed. "Out! Out!" I was shouting now, and the others were afraid, not of the darkness, but of my voice, the voice they knew so well. The hand was still moving, and a quaint bobbing of a white head could be seen nearby. "It's the hand that comes to get me," I cried.

"Be quiet, Sister!" It sounded as though the voice were speaking as the hand moved towards my wrist taking the cord into the fingers that were ready to clamp on it. The hands were white in the darkness and were moving towards my wrist, painfully closing my mouth making me swallow the words that were chattering in the darkness.

"Lie still, Sister, it's only me." More hands, quiet hands were forcing me into the bed. There were hands everywhere, horrible hands, white hands, gentle hands, everywhere hands were moving and I could not control them. There was suddenly a click in the darkness and the match lit the candle the other hands were holding. There were hands all over the walls, grotesque hands, black hands, yet soothing.

The devils began to move out of the room frightened by the flickering halo that surrounded the candle. White hands disappeared behind white sheets, and on the walls they looked like small black mountains swallowing the climbers as they ascended the peak.

They injected a liquid into my arm, where it came from I do not know, it mattered little. Sleep was coming and once more brought hands that pushed the hens into the coop and forced the knife into the potatoes. The roof tops climbed into the room and the dark smoke was everywhere. Suddenly the gulls arose triumphant above the haze and screeched on into freedom.

In the morning they sent the electrician to fix the lamp and they sent me back to the infirmary. No one spoke about the previous night, it was though it had never been. They whispered, I could hear them whispering. No rules could stop the whispering. I heard in that room the first whispering, people speaking about me and smiling pleasantries into my face. But the world had suddenly become faceless. The day was light and the night dark, and there was nothing else.

In the infirmary the Infirmarian was as patient as ever. She sewed by day and at night her companion took up the sewing, and I lay there waiting for the dark, more fearful than I had ever been before. Dreams came with the darkness and release with the dawn. When the cock crew night was betrayed. The song that had cast out Christ whistled Him in for me. The sun that shone on the outside made the white walls whiter. The Infirmarian sat on the chair and I waited. What am I waiting for? I wondered.

"How are you?" the Infirmarian would enquire.

"Quite well, Sister. My arms are weak though, and there is no power in my legs."

"It will come back, don't worry on that score. You're not through yet. There's many a duck that waddles on after a fright."

"I'm not frightened, Sister."

"Maybe not, with me in the chair and the light on full blast. But when the night comes, how are you then? When this fear passes you can talk about not being afraid. Fear is nothing, Sister. Don't be ashamed of fear. It follows us everywhere."

"I wish I were dead." The words were like a whimper and I despised myself. "To be dead is so dark. Is there any darkness to compare with the grave? We are nailed into it then Sister and there is no turning over for light."

"Maybe the Lord will give you a glow-worm, Sister, don't meet trouble before it comes."

Trouble, there was no trouble, death would come on easy wings, it wouldn't be any trouble. We slide into it so easily; shovelled into darkness, smoothed into darkness we enter the grave, the body drawn from the bier like the black ace from the pack. Shuffled and shovelled we enter the darkness where nothing will avail us.

I decided to sleep to meet death half-way. If the glow-worm glowed I would follow the light, but not total darkness. I closed my eyes and heard voices. I would let them drone in the darkness and in the light. I needed neither now. They offered me the light as a prologue to death, to darkness. I had changed the two of these for total greyness. I would never open my eyes again, and succeeded for some days. They threatened me. I heard the medical voices. "Dehydration, Mother Superior, dehydration, that's the worry." Let them worry, I had done the most up to now. "Keep your eyes shut," I thought. "If you listen to them now there is no going back."

"She hasn't eaten for days, doctor."

"It isn't the food, it's the water, Mother Superior." I hoped they would drown in the water. I wouldn't open my eyes. Every so often I could feel the small cup that they offered at my lips. But I rejected it.

One day they tricked me. A doctor whom I had known slightly at the University came to see me. He called me by my Christian name. "Ruth, Ruth." It was as though he had said, "Lazarus, arise." But I closed my eyes. They closed even more tightly as the last hand of the cards was played.

"Ruth, listen to me. The world is full of pain. There are people who are far worse off than you. Listen to me." He knelt by the bed. I could feel his breath on my face. I could hear the words and feel the breath, yet I closed my eyes and my breath.

"The world has so much tragedy. Why can't you help instead of hindering? You can start afresh, you can begin again where things are more suitable."

To me then the various tragedies of which life is composed were of no interest. I couldn't feel sorry for the world. It had beaten me and made me so weak. It had deprived me of life, and left me to swing around the lamp post of twilight without a thought. When I had wanted help from the world, what did it offer me? When I was alone who spoke to me? I had crossed out light and dark from my existence. One flicker of my eyelid would bring them back. My lashes closed in union and kept the words and wiles of the world at bay. I had whisked out the words that the world would utter with my closed lashes that acted like a

169

cow's tail. Where there was no division the enemy came, and I closed my eyes more tightly than ever. I kept them out, all of them. I had long since ceased to worry about the terrible happenings that surrounded me. I was glued into a world that was selfish and I was happy in my misery.

19

A S MY hunger mounted I became weaker. The world was my supplier, death my anaesthetist, but hunger prevailed. I felt like a prisoner betraying my country, but in my need I stretched for their food. As I stretched out for the food it seemed as though I unlatched the hencoop and the black claws came nearer. I turned off the light and started to march on their ruled pavement. I said good-bye to the hills that were my freedom and waved a dismissal farewell to the gulls who escaped on their fleet wings. Hills arose on all sides and I clambered up them and fell continuously. Again and again I tried to mount the side and fell into the ravine below. I swallowed their soup so that I would have the strength to climb, but as I climbed the walls loomed whiter than I had ever seen them before, waiting for messages that they could type on their blank spaces. Would they engrave my story on their white surface —the story of the girl who could not control her eyelids, or the hunger of her belly, was this their tale? When I opened my eyes I knew that it would be a long time before I could close them again.

The walls laughed at me. The floor arose in derision, the ceiling fell down so shaken was it with amusement. As it loomed towards me I really opened my eyes and the battle was over.

"Lord love you, Sister, I thought we would never see you again."

"I never moved, Sister Infirmarian. I was here, always, I never moved. Because I closed my eyes I did not remove my body. It was my soul that went."

"What things you say, Sister. Take the gruel and I'll let Mother Superior know you have woken up at last. She will be pleased." She handed me the gruel and supported the bowl and tidied the sheet with the other hand. I heard her later scurry down the passage.

"She's awake now, Mother, come quickly before she drops off," I heard her saying.

"Off the edge of the world. Dear God let me slope along the edge of the world. Let it be neither light nor dark. Let me have peace, nothing but peace."

Mother Superior came, and with her, total misunderstanding.

"What has happened to you, Sister?"

"I don't really know, Mother, I don't really know." It was the truth. I really didn't know. I wanted them to understand and yet deliberately refused to let them come near me. I had closed my eyes and had dismissed them, and was happy when I had done so. I was like a small child that deliberately threw the ball and then immediately wanted its return.

"I can't explain. Perhaps I don't even know myself. I am deliberately pushing you all away. Perhaps I am throwing off the convent and what it stands for. Perhaps I no longer believe in the discipline and the control. I no longer seem to control myself but am crumbling away like a mountain that the sea has washed brutally so that the founda-

172

tions are no longer secure. I feel that small parts of me are drifting in the sea that has battered me and I will never be so whole again."

"Don't say that, Sister. A little rest and you will be as right as rain. You are only fatigued."

"As right as rain, Mother? The rain drops down and is absorbed by the earth, swallowed and enveloped it disappears. This is what is happening to me. I am falling off the roof tops on out of sight, so tiny that the eye cannot see. I am as weak as the rain drop. There is no right to the rain that I am. I feel that I am being swallowed, that I am disappearing."

"Try to sleep again now, Sister, and in the morning we will get the doctor again. There is nothing some rest cannot conquer. God bless you now, and sleep peacefully."

She went out and automatically switched off the light, and I lay there waiting for the Infirmarian to return and re-light the room.

20

THE ILLNESS did pass as the Mother Superior had said and I eventually left the infirmary, leaving behind the ceiling on which the devils had played. The sun that had surrounded the room with its circle of warmth seemed to disappear.

I was old and drained when I returned to the Community. The nuns acted as though I had never been away.

"I'm glad to see you up again, Sister. Are you quite well now?"

There were letters from many nuns whom I had known only slightly. It was as though the whole province was conspiring to make me well.

I was tired then as I had never been tired. The wakening bell would bring my feet to the floor but it could not make me move. The wash basin seemed a thousand miles away, and my body was heavy and weary. I dressed myself so slowly that I was late every morning in the chapel. No one reprimanded me. I knelt when they knelt, and bowed my head at the Consecration in the Mass, glad just to place my head on my arms. The ceremonies were long and the meditations were a continual battle that I rarely won, and when I did it was no better than fastening one link in a broken bracelet. At every point I was liable to fall down. At every point I was terrified that the dreams would come back or that I would faint. I was then beginning to understand that I could not go on and that all the years of fighting had been useless. Whatever or whoever the opponent was I could not defeat it.

The Mother Superior eventually sent for me.

"It's more rest you need, Sister. A complete change by the sea."

"Whatever you think, Mother Superior."

I wanted someone now to make the decisions, to tell me what to do. I clung on to the advice that was given because it prevented my forcing a choice on my own bemused mind.

I began to think of the sea and the garden where I had found some happiness. I began to think of the small gate that led on to the mountain, where I could join the goats on the hill. In the room where I was kneeling I could hear their pathetic cries as they ran along the mountain edge heavy with their milk. I could see them kicking the dirt as they ran and shaping the hillside with their feet. I saw them rearing their heads and frightening the quiet sheep with their noise. The sheep would run in confusion along the mountain side and look through their half closed eyes at the city that ran beneath. The goats would look out of their eyes dark with mistrust and then butt the friendly earth with joy when they saw that I had come back. When the waves beat the sand and the shore disappeared in fear, then the moments of mad freedom would come again.

I arrived back in the late summer and heard the cry of the gulls as the car drove past the shore. The white house with the beautiful gardens opened its arms as I walked up the ascending path. The Lay Sister opened the door and beamed the monastic welcome. She took my little case and led me into the Superior's room. The Superior in this house who was wise welcomed me with the monastic kiss and blessing and took me into the Community room where the assembled Community greeted me and made room for me.

The days passed in the white sun and moving sea, and I felt the cure of the glowing wind. I moved happily in the curved garden, and saw again the small children who ran in and out of the shadows that the trees threw unknowingly on the earth. The tree world came into the topsy-turvy land of childhood with a control that they only could understand. The upside-down world of trees or parents was all the same to them and I envied. The world began to have a meaning again for me. The days were divided into night and morning. Clear mornings followed nights that began in darkness, and yet soon gave place to the sleep that so often carried me out of the darkened existence. The gulls sent in their song and the waves made their lolling noise when I was so lonely. When I thought of the children I was happy. I saw them running out to the sea that made for them, day after day, the foaming cream that betrayed the tinkling cart only in its taste. But on certain days even the sea sent up its message of disturbance and I felt the old oppression coming back. I walked one day by the little rocks and saw the dirt of disillusion on the foam. Even the sea had its corruption, and I was sad.

I began to feel that I had completed the cycle. I had returned to the convent that had seen me in the autumn of beginning. I heard, in the Senior study, the voices of the girls who had been so small when I had been there previously. Their adolescence was ending, their power over the wheel was increasing, and they were preparing to go out into the world that I had found so difficult.

21

IT COULDN'T last for ever and I knew that soon I would have to return to my own convent and make the decisions I had resolved on as I lay on the small mountain and looked at the sea. Three weeks later when I left the convent I felt sad. I knew the cause but would not admit it. I was sorry to leave the mountain and the freedom. I was sorry to lose the wild feeling that the gulls inspired, but most of all I regretted leaving the convent. I would never return, I would never come back again. The foundations were crumbling and the weakening process that had begun before my illness was progressing. The city with its dirt and noise, unwanted poor, and dishevelled prostitutes and the vagrant merchants was preparing to swallow me and there was nothing I could do. The decision was mine to make. I returned to the city and was greeted by the Superior.

"Are you quite well now, Sister; your old self again?"

"I am my old self again, Mother, that's half the trouble."

"What do you mean?"

"I mean, Mother, that the control I built in the Novitiate has gone. I'm like the man in the Bible who built his house on the quicksand, and now cannot keep the foundations firm. I want what I have lost but there's no retrieving now."

"Are you quite decided then, Sister?"

I never admired her more. There was no attempt at persuasion, no attempt to change my mind. My decision was accepted. They knew that I was the only one to make the decision and they left that to me.

We renewed our vows annually in the early stages of the religious life. They were not vows taken for life, and at the end of every year we were free to go. When I thought of this I saw the chapel with benches carved in dark wood. I heard the voices rising in dedication as the vows were renewed. The day of renewal was one of celebration and the bells in the chapel rang aloud the message that the young nuns had won another round against the world. It was like a special new year for the religious house. They did not drink to the passing of the old but gathered it with the wafered sheaf they had collected, and sipped briefly at the goblet in thanksgiving. This year the four would be reduced to three. Like the old nursery rhyme the numbers would diminish as the bottles were toppled from the wall. This year the shattered glass would surround me, I would be dispersed and fall on the wallside that looked at the passing world.

Later, when I lay in the little white-caged room I could feel the splintered glass cutting into my head. These days the sharp pains in my head were beginning to make thought of all things outside of myself almost impossible. I had never been so concerned with my own pain before. Now the pain was all-surrounding and all-caressing. It seemed to hurt and comfort me at one and the same time.

I did not want to leave them. As the day drew nearer I realised this more and more. They were a group I would never find again on this earth. If I could not survive here where would I survive? If the pains came like sharpened glass in this convent what would the world do to me? I could not face the turmoil. I could not leave. They must push out the walls, they must do something to make it possible for me to stay. I did not want to be an outcast. I could not go back and I could not stay. How could I admit defeat to the family that had seen me lie in dedication in the chapel, where the sea sang the song of glory, when the verses of the *Ecce Sacerdos Magnus* had filled the chapel golden with flowers and joyful in its hope? How could I leave the God to whom I had lain down in dedication? How could He leave me now? I prayed as I had never prayed before. I besought the all-answering God to remove the jagged chalice and give me relief. I had no garden in which to lie down but I suffered the departure a million times. For Christ the flowing of the blood had come on the following day. I was to wait for the separation of body and spirit for many days. I must sit with the look of dedication whilst the body fought for departure.

There was no help now in the decision from the Superior, who saw the life to be too confining, as did the confessor and the Bishop. I had appealed to the Bishop for help and had found him dulled with the dinners that were his work. He did not really notice me when I visited him in his darkened residence. One nun more, or less, in the diocese did not worry him. He was not sure whether he approved of nunneries. The old nuns were useful for taking care of domestic details. No, as far as he could see with his limited sight that came through pompous spectacles there was no reason for me to stay.

After my interview I returned to Christ who was ever present in the Tabernacle, and I besought Him with a strength that had always before eluded me—"Don't let me go!" My prayer seemed to shatter the separating curtain. I must reach Him. I had believed in Him, I did believe in Him. I wanted Him to listen. When He had been in agony I had hidden my face in the blue coverlet and comforted Him, and now His return was to hide His face behind the green curtain. He was a coward in this moment. He could not face me. He was protected by the curtain. He had everything in His favour, and I was left clenching the bench that had held a hundred prayers before mine.

What had they prayed, I wondered, had they suffered a similar agony, had they been kneeling there in the agony that would join with mine and make a rainbow of black and grey in the sky?

I wondered what would happen to the hens when the cold weather came. Would they suffer the frostbite of the land on the hill? Would they lose their feathers in the fight for security? They were not so pathetic as I, for the feather-less hens would at least have companionship, and I had nothing. When I went I went alone, and the group with whom I had built my life would pass for ever from my sight. They would not want me to go. They were all of them close friends and I wondered what they would think when the morning of renewal showed me to be absent. Would they think that I had left for some reason of worldly pleasure? They might think that I had been glad to go. I wanted to tell them. I wanted them to know that I had felt their friendship deeply, and though I would never see them again I would never forget them.

I would see them again when the stars opened and the heavens showed them at last the God who had risen higher in the clouds than the ever-soaring sea-gulls. What of them? Would they come with their swift movement in the garden?

Would they give their haunting cry? Would they wonder what had happened to the summer visitor? The birds and the sea of blowing innocence were moving away from me, and I was left waving the foam on which I had been buoyed a sad good-bye.

The doctor, the Superior and the Bishop had little to offer in hope or comfort. They could not envisage my return, and they were sure that I must go. The walls had won. There was nothing a Superior could do with the crushing walls, and little that the doctor could do against a road that at times opened too wide, and then compensated by closing me tightly under the wheels of the approaching animals.

I could not tell my friends of my departure. The hardest command that had ever been given to me during my time in the convent came with this rule. I had to leave the friends with whom I had shared so much without even the usual salutation that was given when one left the house. To have done this would have made them wonder. One never left the house on the new year of the vows. They were all waiting for the Mass that would give them their chance to make their proclamation in the silent chapel at an hour when the world had not thought of rising. The dedication went on whilst the world slept. They were keeping the God of wrath appeased in the little chapel of the grimy city.

On the eve of the renewal I could not bear the silence any longer, and I went to bed that night in a strange room specially chosen because it was set well apart from the house in which the nuns slept and was comfortable and luxurious. My last rest in the convent was surrounded by the luxuries of the world I despised.

The lay Sister who brought my drink was initiated into

the secret I had been forbidden to share with the others who were my friends. There was here the strange mixture of servant and conspirator, and as I watched the little nun bring in the drink I was overwhelmed with sadness.

The pain and the sadness and the joy I had experienced in my years in the convent followed me on the last night like a pathetic dog. I lay in bed terrified by the thought of the next day, and the pain of the departure filled me. I did not want to go. I wanted to be with the others as they moved in unison on to the steps of the altar in the hour of rising light. As they moved to make their vows I knew I would go. The clock that chimed the hour of their contract released me from mine.

Like a condemned murderer I prayed that I might be spared this hour of terrible separation, and I slept with the doomed prayer on my lips. The black Irish eyes of the Lay Sister penetrated me, and the hand of the old Superior comforted my head where the glass had started the pains again.

The morning came. Death would come with the same inevitability and there would be no escaping. I lay there remembering the first profession day and wept. I wondered would they have all gone if their suffering had been the same? There was again no answer to my question. I did not want them to be forced to this extremity. I would never know the answer to the question. The questions that perplexed me during my stay would never now be answered. The pain, like the questions, would pass, and I would be left without answers, without a guide, and without hope. I could hope for nothing as I lay on the bed in the early hour. I thought back briefly on the little convent and yet could not keep my thoughts there. I had too many memories to be troubled with the old warfare. The old nun had won and I yielded her the victory. She had driven me out. I could never have won where the enemy was so skilled. I couldn't bear to think of her now at this last moment when the roots of my happiness and security were being trundled in the mud. I couldn't waste last memories on her. I would remember the days in the white infirmary and the happy hours spent with the young nuns and the hours spent in theological discussion. I would remember for ever and, on the day of dividing cloud, look for the brown-eyed lay sisters who had worked so hard that we might learn.

As I lay there I heard the bell for the early rising and with unaccustomed sloth I tossed aside the blanketed sound. I did not need to rise with the bell that day, and for ever the bell would throb in my memory without seeking my obedience.

Later when I arose there was no urgency in my dressing. I was waiting in the new room for the change. The gnashing of teeth would start when the wheeled vehicle rounded the path in the God-turned circle and curved on, out of the sound of the bell that was celebrating the renewal of the victory in the garlanded church.

I would leave them all, for ever, as the wheels turned on the outward journey.